PAY DAY

PROCTOR

The VanCleve Ball Homestead

Bertram Guelbh

PAY DAY

"VanCleve Ball,"
A Jeffersonian Democrat Discusses New Dealers, High Taxes, Bureaucrats, Communism

By
DAVID MILTON PROCTOR

BROWN BOOK COMPANY
PUBLISHERS
1016 BALTIMORE AVE.
KANSAS CITY, MO.

First Printing, January, 1936
Second Printing, January, 1936
Third Printing, February, 1936
Fourth Printing, March, 1936
Fifth Printing, April, 1936
Sixth Printing, May, 1936
Seventh Printing, June, 1936

Printed in the United States
by
BROWN-WHITE COMPANY
KANSAS CITY, MO.

18

TABLE OF CONTENTS

8 TABLE OF CONTENTS

FOREWORD

The personality which inspired these letters comprising PAY DAY was a practical farmer born and reared on a north Missouri farm. His father was a Kentucky farmer and his grandfather a Virginia farmer. All three were faithful followers of Thomas Jefferson and loyal Americans. Much of the philosophy and attitude toward public questions reflected in the letters of VanCleve Ball are those of this Missouri farmer, personally and intimately known to the author. Many current statistics have been inserted only to emphasize his wisdom. It is historically true that certain members of the Ball family of Fauquier County Virginia, bore arms against the king in the Revolutionary struggle and were related by blood to Mary Ball, the mother of George Washington. With reference to the numerous quotations, (excepting only a few of them) I feel forced to adopt the graceful language of Montaigne, the French Essayist:

> "I have gathered me a posy of other men's flowers and only the thread that binds them is mine own."

I acknowledge my gratitude to a few faithful friends whose valuable aid, advice, and encouragement has made possible the writing and publishing of PAY DAY.

TO THE YOUTH OF AMERICA,

upon whose shoulders rests the solemn duty of rescuing the United States from the dangers caused by visionary theorists, false leaders, and enemies within our gates, I respectfully dedicate PAY DAY, with an abiding faith they will triumph in their efforts "to preserve, protect, and defend the Constitution of the United States," which guarantees a greater measure of freedom and happiness than any political document known to man.

The Author.

Kansas City, Mo.
Jan. 13, 1936.

VANCLEVE BALL, square-toed and hard-fisted farmer, says in PAY DAY:

We Democrats could sue President Roosevelt for divorce on the grounds of desertion and win.

I do not recall a time when a surplus of crops caused me any acute suffering.

What does it profit a man to gain a few crumbs of dole and lose a whole wagon load of liberty?

President Roosevelt seems to be against dictators and autocrats—in Europe.

You cannot approach the Townsend Plan with thought. You have to go into a trance and dream of it.

They are trying to invent some ointment to take the place of sweat.

Shall we continue to borrow and spend or settle down and settle up?

Jefferson founded the Democratic Party; Roosevelt dumbfounded it.

The New Dealers shipped several carloads of misguided farmers to Alaska to farm among the glaciers and icicles.

I

PRICE TAGS AND PAY DAYS

Huntingdale, Missouri,
September 21, 1932.

Mr. James Ball,
Colvard College,
West Plains, Virginia.

Dear Son:

I have your letter of the 15th. I was glad to learn that you are now pleasantly situated. I am glad you selected Colvard College. For nearly two centuries it has been a fine training ground for men who made their mark in business, the professions and in public life. I noted your request for more funds and I am enclosing my check. Your mother just reminded me that last Thursday was your eighteenth birthday. I realize that in three short years you will reach your majority. I encouraged all four of the children to go to college, but you are the only one who seems to be inclined to do it. John was anxious to go into business and begin making money and the two girls were early weaned away from all thought of higher education by matrimony. I worked my way through college, waiting on the table, but at the end of my Junior year my father died. It was during the '90's. Times were hard. I was forced to leave and give up all hope of a professional career.

I intended to caution you against the **isms** and theories which today are being taught in many colleges and universities. Fifty years ago the West was dotted with little schoolhouses which were red on the outside. Today some of our colleges and universities are becoming a little red on the inside. Some of your young professors may put out some false doctrines. Of course, you will have to listen to them, but—I would stop right there.

At the very outset I want to make plain to you the importance of economy and thrift. To be a spendthrift is a sin. To be a miser is a sin. The compromise between the two is sane economy. Some people practice economy naturally, others are extravagant and never overcome the habit. I remember that forty years ago north Missouri was inhabited both by fox squirrels and gray squirrels in great numbers. Today the gray squirrels are almost extinct. The fox squirrels are still plentiful.

From my own observation, I learned that during the summer and fall months the fox squirrel gathered nuts and either stored them away in the tree containing his nest or buried them in the ground nearby. The gray squirrels seemed to have a different temperament. They paid no heed to approaching winter with its snow and storms. They were carefree and frolicked from morning till night. They stored no food. When winter with its deep snows finally came I have seen gray squirrels wandering a quarter of a mile from their nests toward a corn field, foraging for food. Too many times before they could complete their belated trip they were overtaken and devoured by lean and hungry hounds. You could retouch this picture just a little and make it apply to the human family.

As you grow older you will learn this: everything worthwhile has a price tag. You will never gain anything of value without paying the price. I am not referring to the financial cost of an education. I refer to the work and drudgery which you will be called upon to invest. Ambitions are made of dreams. Success is made of drudgery.

They say Edison was a "wizard." But if you will read the history of his life you will find that he put in about sixteen hours a day for more than sixty years.

You must remember that there is always a pay day. It is the one thing in life from which there is no escape. If you dance you must pay the fiddler; likewise, if you borrow money you must pay your creditor. There is no substitute for payment. You may not pay your debt in coin of the realm. Some even undertake to avoid payment by bankruptcy, by leaving the country, or by repudiating the debt, but none of these methods wipe out the obligation. Thereafter you either pay in mental suffering, or, from a loss of all credit among your fellowmen. Pay day is the night of **hey day.** It never takes on the form of a dream. It is always a stern reality. The bank sends a fancy calendar to me every Christmas. I hardly regard it as a gift, but, just a bundle of nicely arranged pay days.

You may have the false notion, as I know many have, that you can inherit only assets and things of value, but the grim truth is, you can also inherit debts. Upon my death you will not be haled into court to pay any of my debts, but when you reach the age of twenty-one years and become a full-fledged citizen of the United States you will owe your share of the National Debt of the United States, and also your part of the debts of your State, County, City, and School District.

For the last 20 years officials have engaged in a spree of wild spending. They have borrowed money and have signed long term bonds, which will some day fall due. Pay day will arrive and it will be necessary for you to pay your share, whatever it may be. So, everywhere in life, in nature, in business, in government you will be faced on every hand with signs posted on every corner and at all crossroads announcing Pay Day!

Pay day will accept neither excuses nor good intentions. Laying the cash on the barrelhead is the only way. In your plans for the future do not depend on luck. Those who pursue dame fortune are usually mated with **mis**fortune. Throw away your rabbit's foot and carry with you at all times a tuning fork. Learn the fixed laws of nature, as well as the true principles of business morality, then 'tune yourself to them.

Money is so scarce that Anna and the children will not be able to visit us this winter. The campaign is warming up. Our table in the sitting room is loaded with pamphlets received from the various political committees.

With love, I am

Your Dad,

Van Cleve Ball

II

PLATFORM AND PLEDGES

Huntingdale, Missouri,
November 5, 1932.

Mr. James Ball,
Colvard College,
West Plains, Virginia.

My Dear Son:

I was glad to learn that you have adopted the plan of walking three miles a day. This will be a fair substitute for the out-of-door work of the farm. Many farm boys injure their health upon entering college by not adjusting their farm appetites to their scant exercise.

You mentioned joining the students' Jeffersonian Democratic Club. Of course it was proper for you to join. While you will not be old enough to vote at the next election, you will have the benefit of political discussions and will also meet young men who, in years to come, will be the leaders in Virginia and other states.

Your grandfather, who was a real hero-worshipper of Thomas Jefferson, kindled in me almost a reverence for the writer of the Declaration of Independence. While no one has ever accused me of being a politician, I have tried to keep up with political issues and voted at every election. I have always voted the straight Democratic ticket. My first ballot was cast for Grover Cleveland, when he was, for the third time, the Democratic candidate in 1892.

Your grandfather had the honor of voting for Thomas Hart Benton in his last campaign, and also for Douglas and Tilden.

Before you know it, you will be a voter with responsibilities. When I pass on I will not leave for you and the other children much of an estate. I am going to try to make up for this by giving to you in my lifetime the benefit of some things I have learned, from reading, experience and hard knocks.

America is passing through a crisis. I don't know what the outcome will be and therefore I am much disturbed. During your four years at college I expect to write you letters, along serious lines, from time to time. They will be in long hand. If you will keep them they may be a source of some interest to you and other members of the family after I am gone.

Probably you have not had a chance even to read the Democratic Platform which was adopted in Chicago. I believe it is one of the best platforms any political party ever drafted.

I do not refer so much to the planks regarding prohibition repeal and the usual attacks on the Republican party. I refer to the planks covering proposed policies in the matter of debts, budgets, and the farm problem. These concern us most now.

I have clipped from some of the pamphlets extracts from the platform and I am enclosing them. You will note that one of them provides:

> "An immediate and drastic reduction of governmental expenses by abolishing useless commissions and offices, consolidating departments and bureaus and eliminating extravagance, to accomplish a saving of not less than 25% in the cost of Federal government."

This plank is sound. The cost of government has been climbing too rapidly during the last twenty years. I can remember when we had our first "billion dollar Congress." Then the total expenses of our national government, including interest on the debt, was only one billion dollars per year. Now they are more than four billion dollars per year.

Bureaus, boards and commissions have sprung up like mushrooms during the last twenty-five years and they are a curse.

If the author of "The Deserted Village" should

return and spend one day only in Washington, he would probably revise his famous verse to read something like this:

"Ill fares the land
   To hastening ills a prey,
   Where bureaucrats accumulate
   And men decay."

For years I have believed that unless this policy of creating boards and bureaus at every session of Congress is halted, before long the patronage of the party in power will be so great that, when it finishes passing the pie, voting strength of the job-holders will exceed the voting strength of private citizenship.

In other words, I believe that unless we begin to abolish useless boards and bureaus we will soon have an ugly bureaucracy which only the dynamite of a revolution will be able to dislodge.

You will also find this plank among the clippings that I sent you:

"* * * Maintenance of the National credit by a Federal Budget annually balanced on the basis of accurate executive estimates within revenues, raised by a system of taxation levied on the principle of ability to pay."

I endorse this. Private business always suffers when National credit is strained. It is wrong to say that private credit is not affected when the government spends beyond its revenue. That situation always creates a fear which trickles down through the entire business world.

I call your attention to the following plank:

"For the restoration of agriculture, the nation's basic industry, we advocate * * * extension and development of the farm cooperative movement and effective control of crop surpluses so that our farmers may have the full benefit of the domestic market."

I also approve this, although I know that no political party will be able to create an "effective control of crop surpluses," but aside from this language I endorse the plank. I call your attention to two very short but important planks which are as follows:

"A sound currency to be preserved at all hazards. * * *

"Removal of government from all fields of private enterprise."

While Franklin D. Roosevelt knows nothing of farming in the Middle West and its problems, yet I believe that he possesses a sincere desire to do everything in his power, if elected, to promote the welfare of all citizens, including the farmers. He has delivered some speeches which impressed

me. They rang with patriotism. They convinced
me that he has a grasp of the problems which
will confront him as president.

Mr. Roosevelt in his speech of acceptance at
Chicago, said:

> "With reference to the platform, I accept
> it 100%."

In his speech at Pittsburg, November 4th, he
said:

> "I regard reduction in federal spending
> as one of the most important issues in this
> campaign. In my opinion, it is the most
> direct and effective contribution that gov-
> ernment can make to business."

And, in another part of the same speech Mr.
Roosevelt said:

> "* * * The Democratic platform specif-
> ically declares:
> > 'We advocate a sound currency
> > to be preserved at all hazards.'
> That is plain English."

If this platform develops into a kind of disap-
pearing bed like the one Anna has in her flat,
I will be the most disappointed man in Missouri.

The Republicans have controlled things for
nearly twelve years. For the good of all we need
a change. A new broom sweeps clean and I am

convinced we will choose a new broom on November 7th.

Personally, I trust that Franklin D. Roosevelt
will be a worthy successor to Jefferson, Jackson,
Cleveland, and Wilson. He has never had the
common touch. He knows nothing of the grime
of the factory or the sweat of the field, but I believe he is ambitious to make a record.

I am working in the campaign. I have signed
up with the County Committee, agreeing to haul
voters to the polls next Tuesday.

With love and affection,

Your Dad,

VanClere Ball

III

FEDERAL AID NOT A "GIFT"

Huntingdale, Missouri,
November 27, 1932.

Mr. James Ball,
Colvard College,
West Plains, Virginia.

Dear Son:

I was not alarmed when we failed to receive a letter last week. Your mother was sure that you were sick, but I knew that you had gone to a football game.

Your description of Prof. Boley and Prof. Redwell was interesting. Don't let them lead you astray with any of their half-baked theories.

I was glad to learn you had decided upon the law for your profession. I had an ambition to be a lawyer, but as you know, I failed to realize it. I contented myself with farming, and satisfied my thirst for knowledge by reading, through the years, a few good books, magazines, and newspapers. Good books are always an asset. One of the best things about books is that the upkeep is not heavy.

I won't burden you with a lot of advice. It is easy to criticize people. It is almost as easy to give advice. You have the necessary qualities for a career at the bar. You have integrity, ambition, and average intelligence. That is more than a fair start.

I have a few suggestions, however, which might be helpful. You will meet difficulties on the road and, many obstacles. You will have troubles, sometimes they will come singly, sometimes in droves. It is common to label all troubles as adversities. This is a mistake. Most troubles develop character. To meet them, of course, you must retain your courage and make up your mind in advance to stand up to the rack, hay or no hay; as they say, "take it on the chin and smile," and then be thankful that you don't have a double chin. I wish to caution you, however, not to smile all the time. A chronic smile always reminds me of a comic false face that has stuck.

You should remember that our sturdy ancestors of Virginia, nearly one hundred and fifty years ago, conquered the empire extending from the Alleghenies to the Rockies. It was inhabited by Indians and wild beasts. In three generations this pioneer stock from which you sprang, through courage, faith, and determination, overcame the Indians, cleared the forests, spanned the rivers, built railroads, highways, parks, churches, schools, libraries, and homes. They did this single handed and alone, without any aid from the government, except the establishment of an Indian fort here and there. They had no boards or bureaus to pamper, advise, or guide them. Had they been thus handicapped they probably would have failed.

If you ever have an opportunity, I want you to go to Monticello to see the tomb of Thomas Jefferson. You may recall that he prepared and wrote his own epitaph, which, after his death, was inscribed upon his monument and it is as follows:

"HERE WAS BURIED
THOMAS JEFFERSON
Author of the Declaration of American Independence, of the Statute of Virginia, for religious freedom, and father of the University of Virginia."

He was a wise statesman. He knew he would be remembered in history on account of what he had given **to** society and not by reason of any honors which he had received **from** society. I am sure you will never find a tomb-stone with an inscription which lists the assets acquired during the lifetime of the deceased.

With love,

Your Dad,

VanClere Ball

P. S.

Your mother told me today that you wanted to send to me the "Life of John Marshall" for Christmas. I appreciate your thoughtfulness, but you must not do this. A gift from you would be like Federal Aid we hear so much about these days. It would put you in debt to buy the gift and burden me to pay for it. Federal Aid is a "gift" from our public servants with a price tag. It doesn't come C. O. D. but the bill for it is always enclosed and PAY DAY is stamped on it in red letters.

The election is over. I trust the clouds of depression will soon rise and normal conditions return. The president should appoint a strong cabinet. I have in mind such men as Governor Ely, John W. Davis, Owen D. Young, Alfred E. Smith, Newton D. Baker, Governor Albert Ritchie, Senator Carter Glass, James A. Reed, Bainbridge Colby, and a few other men of that type. If he should fail to surround himself with the strongest available men it will be costly, both to him and to the country. You cannot operate a big business with small men. You cannot haul a load of cord wood over a dirt road with Shetland ponies. For that work you need big Missouri mules.

The country is too large and its problems too complex to be operated by any one man. I believe that Providence intended that all civilized peoples should have the blessings of a democracy.

Dad.

IV

THE TOLL GATE SECTION

Huntingdale, Missouri,
December 26, 1932.

Mr. James Ball,
Colvard College,
West Plains, Virginia.

Dear Son:

We missed you yesterday at our Christmas dinner. Your mother and I, of course, wanted you to be here, but the expense of the trip would have been too great.

Your Uncle Jim and Aunt Martha had dinner with us. Your Uncle Jim was still happy and gloating over Roosevelt's great victory. He celebrated by eating more than usual. When we flooded his plate with gravy for the third time he remarked that he was very fond of gravy and said: "I think gravy is the backbone of our nation."

Your mother replied that our nation needed plenty of backbone and a lot of thickening and stiffening in it.

You asked my advice about your taking certain courses offered. I am not qualified to advise you.

You will have to learn to use your own judgment in such matters. You are on the ground. I am not. I do not want to confuse you with suggestions that might be off-key.

In this matter of individual judgment I wish you would read Woodrow Wilson's History of the American People. In the first volume you will find that Wilson tells why the English were so successful in colonizing America. * * * He wrote:

> "England licensed trading companies and left the colonists, who went to America in their own interest, to serve that interest by succeeding in their own way. The English colonies, throve under 'a wise and salutary neglect.' * * * The task called for hard-headed business sense, patient, practical sagacity, and men free to follow their own interest by their own means." * * *

So, in all matters in which you are the best judge my policy will be that of "wise and salutary neglect."

Your decision to become a lawyer was probably a wise one. I had a secret ambition to see you follow in my footsteps and take charge of this farm some day. On the other hand, from your standpoint I could not urge you to do it. Farming is not as promising now as it was 40 years ago when I began it upon my own account. From 1898 to 1920 farming was fairly profitable. The profits came, however, more from the increase in the value of our lands than from any net revenue derived from the operation of them. You know that the St. Louis Cardinals sometimes have a "losing streak." We farmers have had a losing streak for many years.

Many years ago they began increasing freight rates. We farmers of the West caught the full brunt of it. The states which do not enjoy the convenience of water transportation and the benefit of water rates, are known as the "toll gate section" of the country. The farmers annually pay hundreds of millions of dollars for the one item of freight alone.

I will have to close this letter. I must do the chores before dark.

With love, I am

Your Dad,

VanClene Ball

Dec. 27, 1932.

P. S.

It is snowing this afternoon; however, we are pretty well prepared for winter. We would not suffer if a snow three feet deep should fall. Our cellar is filled with Irish and sweet potatoes, turnips, pumpkins, and cabbage. Our fruit closet is running over with apples, molasses, honey, cider, and several hundred quarts of preserves which your mother put up last summer.

We have killed hogs and the smoke house is filled with hams and bacon. There are several cords of dry wood sawed, split and piled high in the wood house.

There is plenty of hay, and grain in the barn to carry the livestock through the winter. Some "farm leaders" who are always looking for new problems, have been worked up over crop surpluses. Personally, I have no objection to a little surplus. In fact, I do not recall a time when a surplus of crops caused me any acute suffering.

We received a letter from Anna yesterday. She paints a terrible picture. She said that architects are almost literally starving to death in Chicago. Many of the politicians have told us that the farmers were suffering more than any other people, but I doubt this. There must be, in the large cities, millions of people who are faring worse than the farmers, as a class.

Dad.

V

QUACK FARM DOCTORS

Huntingdale, Missouri,
January 10, 1933.

Mr. James Ball,
Colvard College,
West Plains, Virginia.

My Dear Son:

We received your letter stating that you had received the barrel of apples. I hope that you will have much pleasure in sharing them with your friends.

I agree with you that the farmers have had some bad breaks. The farmers had their crash in 1920-21. Prices of land and livestock fell overnight. You could not call it a decline; they fell almost straight down in 1920-21 visiting losses upon thousands of farmers. Nine out of ten ranchmen and cattle feeders were bankrupted. Farmers who bought lands at war prices and mortgaged them, were foreclosed. The Federal Reserve Bank Board, who lost their heads, had much to do with this sudden drop in farm prices.

I remember that in May 1920, during President Wilson's second administration the Federal

Reserve Bank Board virtually forced all member banks to "call" their farm and cattle loans immediately. Farms and livestock were dumped pell-mell upon the market. This caused the crash of 1920-21.

The sad condition of the farmers at that time stirred the hearts of the so-called "farm leaders." From that date to this, these "farm leaders" and what I call "quack farm doctors" have surrounded congress and demanded legislation to "relieve and aid" the farmer. These new "friends" convinced a majority of congressmen that the rank and file of the farmers was behind their new cure-alls. This was not true, and is not true today.

Many people under-estimate the intelligence of the farmers. On an average they are better informed than the people who reside in the cities. They give more time to the problems which involve them than do the residents of the big centers. Their outside interests are fewer; they read newspapers and market reports more carefully and listen to addresses over radios. Consequently, as a class, they are more fully informed about daily events than their cousins in the cities.

When you were four or five years old citizens of the county sent me to the legislature. During my first term two bills, which would have destroyed the grain and livestock commission businesses of Missouri, were introduced. I opposed them and voted against them. I named one of the bills "Lenin," and the other "Trotsky," because of many unfair provisions.

In Chicago, St. Louis, Kansas City, and other large stock and grain centers, commission firms have been built upon a foundation of fair dealing. During the last 30 years one of the most pleasant parts of my business has been that whenever I sent a carload of livestock to market I received for my shipment prompt service and cash on the barrelhead the following day.

It is quite probable that the new Congress will prescribe some new patent medicine for the farmers. If it does, it will not cure the ailments. The politicians who weep upon the shoulder of the farmer, and these quack farm doctors will never cure our ills.

In the first place, they do not understand the problems. Their only concern is holding jobs. They are in the business of trading spurious legislation for votes. For years they have traded us ashes for coal, and in the deal, they have made us farmers deliver the coal and carry the ashes out. They have cluttered up the situation. They have almost doctored us to death. Sometimes they wake us up at night to give us a dose of some fake medicine.

We farmers would be better off if Congress would let us alone for a few years. If, in voting for a congressman I had to choose between a Rip Van Winkle and a Pied Piper, I would vote for Rip Van Winkle.

We are having some disagreeable weather but spring will come before we know it.

Affectionately,

Your Dad,

VanClere Ball

VI

PANIC AND DEPRESSION

Huntingdale, Missouri,
February 10, 1933.

Mr. James Ball,
Colvard College,
West Plains, Virginia.

Dear Son:

In your last letter you referred to the bank failures as evidence that "individual initiative" has been a failure. You must realize that you are in an atmosphere of theories. We have had bank failures and depressions about every twenty years since the days of George Washington. There is nothing sacred about a bank. It is a human institution like all other businesses. There are good bankers and bad bankers; some of them successful and some of them unsuccessful. In this country there is nothing unusual about a depression.

I didn't vote the Republican ticket. I do not believe in the farm board plan but will not hold the Republicans responsible in any way for the crash of 1929 or the panic and depression which followed.

We were headed for a depression in 1914. The

World War came upon us, creating a demand for our products, and postponing the day of the depression which was then due. In a little more than four years 100 billion dollars in property and 10 million lives were sacrificed in the explosion and the world is still paying the price of that costly and bloody venture. After a violent explosion in a neighborhood it takes years to replace the broken glass and repair the cracked walls and damaged foundations. We have inherited from the World War the longest pay day I have ever seen.

The United States loaned to foreign countries about 13 billion dollars and expended 12 billion dollars on its own account to save the world for democracy. A large part of these funds was used to purchase products of the American farm and factory. In addition, we paid them many billions of dollars for American securities which they had previously owned. Farm lands worth $75 per acre leaped to $250 per acre. Not being used to such sudden rises in values we imagined that we had become rich overnight. Nearly everyone began buying nearly everything. Millions of Americans bought articles they did not need with money they did not have; and, for these they pledged their incomes, wages and salaries for years in advance.

We were in a fool's paradise and did not know it. We toyed with dynamite and refused to recognize it. Merchants filled their shelves to the ceiling. States, counties and cities everywhere voted bonds for expensive highways and ornamental bridges. New school houses provided with swimming pools and other frills were built at a high level of prices. This wild spending spree continued for ten years. Finally, the people realized that they had over-bought and over-borrowed. We ourselves invited panic and depression. They came and brought the children. Defaults became the order of the day. Confidence was shaken. The bubble burst. Fear spread over the land. The depression was on. Pay day had arrived!

This is only a rough outline of the events which led to the depression. Our form of government had nothing to do with it. It was a combination of inflation, greed and speculation. Our so-called prosperity was the disease. Depression is the cure. This cure, though painful, will save the country. We have the same wealth now that we had before the depression. We have the same quantity of land. American people as a whole possess the same ideals, courage and industry. Confidence only is lacking.

With love and affection,

Your Dad,

Vaullene Ball

VII

PRESIDENT ROOSEVELT'S OATH

Huntingdale, Missouri,
March 13, 1933.

Mr. James Ball,
Colvard College,
West Plains, Virginia

Dear Son:

I have just finished sowing oats. When I came to the house I found your mother pottering around her little flower bed. She pointed to the jonquils. Jonquils are always punctual—just like pay days.

I heard President Roosevelt take the oath of office one week ago last Saturday. I came into the house about twelve o'clock and turned on the radio. Almost immediately Chief Justice Hughes began to administer the oath of office. It was the first inaugural service I ever heard. I was not only impressed but deeply moved. Perhaps I am a little too partisan but I regard the event as the beginning of a new day in government and business recovery. As long as I live I will never forget the voice of Franklin D. Roosevelt as he said:

"I do solemnly swear that I will faith-

fully execute the office of President of the
United States and will, to the best of my
ability, preserve, protect and defend the
Constitution of the United States."

Shortly after the ceremony I took from the shelf
one of Woodrow Wilson's books containing a copy
of the Constitution of the United States and I have
read it through four or five times during the last
week. To my surprise I learned that the president's oath is set out word for word in the Constitution itself. I had always supposed that it was
prepared by the Supreme Court but the framers of
the Constitution apparently did not wish to take
any unnecessary chances. They were unwilling
to leave it to some notary public or even to the
Supreme Court to decide on the wording of this
particular oath. Every president of the United
States, from George Washington to Franklin D.
Roosevelt, has taken the same identical oath. Becoming so interested in it I want to discuss it
further with you. I am sure you will not take
the time to analyze it yourself.

Another fact which I was surprised to learn
was that the first Article of the Constitution deals
with Congress and not with the presidency. The
first sentence following the preamble is:

"All legislative powers herein granted
shall be vested in a Congress of the United

States which shall consist of a Senate and
a House of Representatives."

I had real pleasure in reading, and in my own
way, studying the powers and duties which our
forefathers gave to Congress in comparison with
those which they gave to the president. The big
four of the Constitutional Convention were Washington, Franklin, Hamilton and Madison. The following are the duties and powers which these men
and others of the Convention gave to Congress:

To lay and collect taxes.
To pay the debts.
To provide for the common defense.
To provide for the general welfare of the United
    States.
To borrow money.
To regulate commerce.
To establish uniform rule of naturalization.
To establish uniform laws of bankruptcy.
To coin money and regulate the value thereof.
To fix the standard of weights and measures.
To provide for punishment of counterfeiting.
To establish postoffices and post roads.
To promote the progress of science by securing
    to authors and inventors exclusive rights.
To constitute tribunals inferior to the Supreme
    Court.
To define and punish piracy.
To declare war.

To raise and support armies.

To provide and maintain a navy.

To provide for calling forth the militia to execute the laws.

To provide for organizing, arming and disciplining the militia.

To exercise exclusive legislation in all cases over such district (not exceeding 10 miles square) as may become the seat of government.

To make all laws which will be necessary and proper for carrying into execution the foregoing powers.

Now I want you to compare the powers and duties which our forefathers gave to Congress with those which they gave to the president exclusively. The second Article of the Constitution deals with the duties of the president and it provides that he shall take an oath which I have mentioned; after which he has the following powers and duties:

He shall be the commander-in-chief of the army and navy (of course there can be neither army nor navy unless Congress shall authorize it.)

He shall have power to grant reprieves and pardons.

He shall have power to make treaties (with the advice and consent of the Senate.)

He shall nominate and appoint ambassadors, other public ministers, judges of the

Supreme Court and all other officers of the United States (with the advice and consent of the Senate.)

He shall have power to fill up all vacancies that may happen during the recess of the Senate by granting commissions (but said commissions shall expire at the end of their next session).

He shall, from time to time, give to Congress information of the state of the Union.

He may, on extraordinary occasions, convene both houses or either of them.

He shall receive ambassadors and other public ministers. (This designates him as official chairman of the reception committee.)

Lastly, he shall take care that the laws be faithfully executed (he is without authority to enact a single statute).

By a glance at these two lists of powers and duties it is plain that our forefathers intended that Congress should be the real governing body of the United States. In fact, James Monroe once said:

"The whole system of the national government may be said to rest essentially on the powers granted to this branch." (Referring to Congress.)

Why didn't the framers of the Constitution give to the president the full responsibility of running the government? That would have been a simple way of handling it. It wouldn't have taken a week to write the Constitution along those lines.

They were wise men. They had suffered under a king. They knew the records of dictators. For their liberties they had paid a big price and they wanted to protect their investment. I believe they were actually afraid to put much power into the hands of one man.

So, they set up a Congress as a sort of insurance policy. In addition to giving to it numerous important duties they provided that the members of the House should be selected every two years, directly by the people, from every nook and cranny in the country. This was intended as safe insurance against the calamity that would come from the election of either a weakling or tyrant, as president.

Our forefathers who figured out this protection are gone. We, the beneficiaries, are here. It is our job to keep up the insurance and to prevent the storing of any dynamite on the premises. If we fail in this, the insurance policy will lapse.

Woodrow Wilson once said:

"The history of liberty is a history of the limitation of governmental power. Not the increase of it. When we resist, therefore, the concentration of power, we are resisting the processes of death because concentration of power is what always precedes the destruction of human liberties."

In a nutshell, they drafted a form of government in which the citizens would be masters and not slaves.

With love.

Your Dad,

Vaullene Ball

P. S. Before mailing this letter I want to give you another thought with reference to the Constitution. I am in favor of amending the Constitution at any time when conditions warrant it, but I will never be in favor of changing our present system of government. I sometimes think that great men of the past and even of other countries appreciate our Constitution more than we do. You will remember that Stephen A. Douglas, the "Little Giant," on his deathbed said:

"Tell them (my sons) to obey the laws and support the Constitution of the United States."

William Pitt, the English statesman, once said:

"It, (referring to the Constitution), will be the wonder and admiration of all future generations and the model of all future constitutions."

Dad.

VIII

THE NEW DEAL CABINET

Huntingdale, Missouri,
April 30, 1933.

Mr. James Ball,
Colvard College,
West Plains, Virginia.

My Dear Son:

I received your letter written during the bank holiday. I did not answer it immediately because this is, as you know, the busy season on the farm.

Ruth, Charlie and the baby have come to live with us, probably only temporarily. I sympathize with Ruth. Charlie does not seem to be able to hold any job. He is a good boy but is unable to hit the proper stride. In the first place, as soon as he obtains employment he applies for an increase in his wage. He regards his services more highly than do his employers. He is always just a little above the market.

Furthermore, he has a keen sense of leisure. He is now trying to get some kind of a political appointment. If he succeeds it will enable him to maintain his family for at least a time, but in the end it will be a calamity. From my viewpoint political jobs are will-o'-the-wisps which decoy and mislead many young men.

I am skeptical about devaluing the dollar. The President will gather up all of the gold in the United States and lock it up in government vaults. Those who protest giving up their private property will be threatened with fines and imprisonment. My grandfather told me that in his day they put men in jail for debt. Times have changed. They now threaten to put us in jail if we have a little gold laid away for a rainy day. The emergency which exists may possibly call for these methods but personally, some of them appear a little high-handed to me.

Mr. Morgenthau, assistant to Secretary of the Treasury, Mr. Woodin, says that the government, by increasing the value of gold from $20.67 an ounce to $35.00 an ounce, will realize a profit of $2,800,000,000. This would be trick bookkeeping. It would not increase the supply of gold nor the real value of it. If President Roosevelt should change the number of pecks in a bushel from four to eight he would not affect the supply of wheat in the country. He would merely decrease the size of a peck of wheat.

Measuring sticks should be certain and fixed. The framers of the Constitution even provided that Congress should have the power to fix a "standard of weights and measures." No standard should be flexible; no honest standard can be flexible. You can't depend on a rubber yardstick.

I will never forget what Henry Bush said when he returned from Alaska in search of gold in 1898. Upon his return he reported a fairly successful trip; that he had made $50.00 a day but, the trouble was, the days were six months long, and coffee cost a dollar a cup.

I am disappointed with the President's cabinet, consisting of nine men and one woman. They are fine citizens but lack the caliber and experience for their chosen positions.

Mr. Wallace is a theorist. He is not a practical farmer. He inherited a farm paper from his father. He will not develop into a Moses to lead us farmers out of Egypt and bondage.

The President needs a cabinet of men who will advise, and not merely sit around him and purr.

Affectionately,

Your Dad,

Vauclene Ball

IX

CONGRESS—AN EXPENSIVE SHOW

Huntingdale, Missouri,
May 15, 1933.

Mr. James Ball,
Colvard College,
West Plains, Virginia.

Dear Son:

I was glad to learn that you had a job for the summer. While your salary is only $15.00 per week it will insure a living and you will probably be able to save $25.00 per month to apply on your expenses this Fall. No one knows what this opening may bring.

I am not able to entirely finance your education this winter. We are helping Anna and her family in Chicago and Ruth and her family are living with us. I will not mortgage my farm. I will borrow all I can on my personal note at the bank to assist you, but you would not expect me, I am sure, to mortgage the farm. For years your mother and I have worked hard. This farm is the only insurance we have for our old age.

I agree with you that it appears that Congress has almost given up its charter and gone out of business. They say that an "emergency" exists and that quick action is required.

Well, if Congress can at any time declare that an "emergency" exists which justifies violating the plain provisions of the Constitution, then we have no Constitution. Our "Civil Bible" as Alfred E. Smith calls it, is just a framed motto hung over the door of our home, to be taken down and damaged every time we clean house.

When you were about seven I remember we left you alone for a few hours one afternoon. Your mother had inherited a grandfather's clock from her father. For fifty years it had kept perfect time. Naturally you were curious. While we were gone you took the clock to pieces. The dial, hands, pendulum, weights, and other parts were scattered all the way from the hall to the wood house. We hired a jeweler to put it together but it has never kept good time since. It is only ornamental and in no way serviceable, because it is not reliable. Inexperienced hands should not be permitted to tinker with delicate machinery, be it a clock or a constitution.

I have been looking for an explanation of the conduct of Congress in frittering away its powers to the point where now our government is just a two cylinder machine. We have lost one cylinder almost completely and have only the executive and judicial cylinders left. I am satisfied that the primary system which we use in selecting congressmen to represent us is largely responsible.

Many primary contests have proven satisfactory, but the fact remains that the judgment of a body of delegates in a convention is more dependable than the blind guess of a primary.

Nowadays many of the candidates seeking nomination for Congress promise everything to everybody. They advocate higher prices for all commodities and reduction in the cost of living. They promise expensive public improvements for the nation, state and county and a deep cut in taxes. When they go to Washington they join hands around the treasury and begin pumping appropriations out of it as though it were a town pump. The people must do something to stop this humbuggery.

Not long ago I read a speech on the primary system which had been delivered by a lawyer in St. Louis. I call your attention to the clipping containing a portion of his speech:

"Every fair-minded person must now be convinced that the primary system as a recoil from the sporadic abuses of the convention system has proved disastrous. We are burning down the barn to catch the rat. It has increased government in our business and decreased business in our government.

It has at once robbed the people of the right
to draft the most attractive talent and has
set mediocrity upon a pedestal. Under it
mountebanks and demagogues are prosper-
ing while modesty and merit languish in
oblivion. Under it conservatism has been
discredited and radicalism enthroned. Con-
test of qualifications is frequently over-
shadowed by a battle of purses. Advocates
of sound principles have yielded the stage
to a troupe of nimble opportunists who well
nigh daily present their repertoire of fantastic fads and schemes.

It has increased the burdens of government, sent our taxes skyward, thus threat-
ening the paralysis of industry and the con-
fiscation of property. It is quietly and in-
sidiously undermining the very foundations
of our government. Political candor and
fortitude have been abandoned and are now
almost obsolete, while political cowardice
and hypocrisy attract the multitude and win
the votes."

When President Roosevelt asked Congress to
transfer to him important powers Congressmen
complied, not because they thought it was their
duty or right. They did it because they thought
President Roosevelt was popular with the people
and they were looking forward to riding into office at the next election on his coat-tails.

Congress, for years, has been developing into
one of the finest trained animal shows in the coun-

try. People from far and near go to watch it, to see them jump through the hoop, roll over and play dead. This competition has bankrupted the Gentry Brothers dog show.

I shudder at the thought of placing so much political power in the hands of one man.

With love, I am

Your Dad,

Vanllens Ball

P. S. We sheared sheep last week. "Bony" came up as usual, just in time to take charge of it. Poor "Bony" still thinks he is Napoleon. It was amusing as well as pathetic to hear him talking to the sheep in the pen, calling them "my prisoners of war." I gave him a check Saturday night. He went straight to a New Deal beer saloon, in town, to "relax."

My flock of sheep still keep the weeds mowed as well as a six-foot mower could do it. In other words, I am paying part of my taxes with weeds. Sheep on a farm remind me of desirable boarders. They are prompt pay and eat little.

Dad.

X

DUMPING LITTLE PIGS

Huntingdale, Missouri,
September 11, 1933.

Mr. James Ball,
Colvard College,
West Plains, Virginia.

My Dear Son:

It has been several weeks since I wrote you. We have not heard from you for a month. You have had long hours and so have I, but after the first of August I feel justified in enjoying a little breathing spell, because usually by that time we have finished our rush work.

Business conditions appeared to improve this summer. There was more confidence. The statement of the President made shortly after his inauguration that he would reduce the cost of government gave business some courage. I understand that the father of the bank guaranty deposit bill, which I believe is a good one, is Senator Vandenberg of Michigan, a Republican. If the bill becomes a law, however, I am not going to worry about its pedigree.

Under an order of the Agricultural Department

millions of little pigs are being shipped to the large markets, where capacities are being overtaxed. Yesterday I read in a Kansas City paper that 75% of 100,000 pigs, weighing from 35 to 80 pounds each, arriving at the Kansas City market had been discarded. The government planned to convert them into fertilizer, grease, and other by-products. With reference to the situation in East St. Louis the paper said:

> "So great was the rush to market, however, that tankage facilities were swamped and much meat was thrown into the Mississippi River or carted to dumps."

They are slaughtering train loads of brood sows. Wholesale destruction of hogs, when millions of people barely have sufficient food to maintain life is unpardonable. Remember, that all of these hogs and pigs were bought and paid for by the Government. If they continue this insane policy it will not be long before we will be importing meat from Argentine, wheat from Canada and food stuffs from all over the world.

I hope that you will get some kind of employment during the winter.

With lots of love,

Your Dad,

Van Clene Ball

P. S.   Charlie has just been appointed to a political job.   It has something to do with Federal
relief.   His jurisdiction is the County.   The salary, I understand, will be about $125.00 per month
and expenses.   I do not see any necessity for any
Federal relief agents in this County.   We have a
few needy people but they can all be cared for
through the County Court and private charity.   I
have wondered if this was for the purpose of buying votes.

                              Dad.

XI

"OWED TO UNCLE SAM"

Huntingdale, Missouri,
September 20, 1933.

Mr. James Ball,
Colvard College,
West Plains, Virginia.

Dear Son:

Yesterday as I read the local paper I was much impressed with the article entitled "Owed to Uncle Sam." Evidently it was intended as a New Deal version of the 23rd Psalm. It contains considerable food for thought. You might be interested in reading it. The article proves that the people are becoming aroused over the policies of this administration. The dumping of pigs into the Mississippi River was so insane that the people will not soon forget it. I wonder who advised those plans.

The local merchants, I understand, are opposed to the Blue Eagle, which is the trade mark of the N.R.A. They say it helps the large companies and chain stores but it is a burden to the small merchant. According to Washington, its purpose is to increase the price of factory products. It is argued that this will enable the manufacturer to pay higher wages, which will increase the purchasing power of the public. Increased purchasing power of the public will, to complete the circle, speed up the wheels of industry.

In theory this may be a good plan. In practice it will not work out. It is placing the cart before the horse. It is an attempt to raise ourselves by our own bootstraps. An immediate increase in the price of manufactured products will delay recovery. The proposed method is not the proper way to prime the pump. Even at the present low price levels, as a matter of fact, there is very little demand now for factory products. How can you increase the purchase and consumption of such products by increasing the price?

The American people will not buy anything merely for the purpose of "aiding recovery." Assuming that they are able, they will buy only when they are compelled to buy or when the price is attractive.

Here is the "Owed":

"OWED TO UNCLE SAM"

"Uncle Sam is my succor, I shall not want;
  He leadeth me into strange pastures,
  Beside the still factories;
  He hoardeth my gold;

He controlleth my wage, and reduceth my
        acreage,
And raiseth the cost of my daily bread.
He anointeth my purse with dole,
He restoreth my soil with trees,
And with the bones of infant swine;
My stein runneth over;
He buildeth roads, ploweth under crops,
Createth codes, banks, bonuses, funds and
        allotments,
Pryeth into my business from morn till
        night,
Flirteth with inflation from week to week,
And daily offereth spurious cures for natu-
        ral ills.
Though my taxes forever mount,
Yea, even though I walk through
The Valley of the shadow of debt,
I will fear no evil, for Thou art with me;
Thy Boards and Thy Bureaus, they comfort
        me,
Blessed be the name of Uncle Sam;
But may Thy Constitution stand the strain,
and Thy pay day be postponed,
Forever and Forever, Amen."

Affectionately, I am

        Your Dad,

    Van Cleve Ball

P. S. You will observe that the author of the
"Owed" had pay day on his mind.

        Dad.

XII

"SWARMS OF OFFICERS"

Huntingdale, Missouri,
October 15, 1933.

Mr. James Ball,
Colvard College,
West Plains, Virginia.

My Dear Son:

All of us were glad to hear that you had been appointed night librarian. The story of your appointment proves that it always pays to be courteous. You treated the librarian courteously when he stopped at the filling station. As a result of your thoughtfulness he invited you to his home, became acquainted with you and your financial condition. A salary of $25.00 per month, coupled with what I will be able to send, guarantees your schooling for at least one more year.

A few days ago I saw the government agents conferring with some of our local merchants and trying to explain to them the "code." I thought of the conditions under which our forefathers suffered, prior to the time of the Declaration of Independence. You will recall that Thomas Jefferson, in that document, used these words:

"He (George III), has erected a multitude of new offices and sent hither swarms of officers to harass our people and eat out their substance."

When I voted for Roosevelt I felt sure he favored the doctrine of states' rights. When he was Governor of New York he made a speech (which I read) preaching the doctrine of states' rights. I thought his views were wonderful. This New Deal legislation, however, confuses me. The President seems now to believe that all problems, financial and economic, can be solved only by theorists in Washington.

I am about ready to believe that the administration has conducted an investigation and "found" that all of us people are incompetent to handle our own affairs. Having so found, it has appointed guardians to look after every detail of our business. Did you notice that Senator Byrd of Virginia recently said:

"Prosperity will never return by the waving of magic wands or by legislative panaceas but only by the independence and ability of the people themselves.

"Under the reign of the Czars of Russia no person could build an addition to his house, even in a remote part of the Empire, without first obtaining permission from some underling in St. Petersburg. Is America coming to this?"

That statement contains sound reasoning. Senator Byrd is a Virginia Democrat and I respect his opinion highly. The government should regulate but not operate any business; it should foster but not father any industry. The Blue Eagle and the American Eagle will never mate.

With love, I am
>Your Dad,

VanClene Ball

P. S. Henry Bush was killed last week and his two sons badly injured in an automobile wreck. I cannot understand all of this haste on the highways. Business conditions do not justify a speed of over eight miles an hour.

>Dad.

XIII

"RELIEVED" ALMOST BEYOND RECOVERY

Huntingdale, Missouri,
November 10, 1933.

Mr. James Ball,
Colvard College,
West Plains, Virginia.

Dear Son:

I had some business in Hannibal yesterday. We drove down on 36 Highway. After I finished my business I visited the Mark Twain cave, for the first time in my life.

Returning home I was reminded that General John J. Pershing and Gen. Enoch H. Crowder were born on Missouri farms, as was Mark Twain.

I merely refer to these men that you may know that the geography of your birth should not in any way affect your ambitions, and your great success in life. In the past the sky has been the limit in America for ambitious young men, whether they came from rich families or those of humble means.

Lincoln and Edison were both born on farms

and in poverty. This did not handicap them. It probably gave them just the grim determination they needed to carve out great careers. Had any of these men mentioned been born in luxury the world probably would have been deprived of their service to society.

I am becoming alarmed at the administration. It has too many schemes. Mr. Roosevelt and his advisers seem determined to relieve us at any price. In their big heartedness I feel that they will eventually hug us to death. They have placed a whole basket of eggs under each one of a large flock of queer looking hens. None of these eggs, however, will hatch. The hens cackle too much. They will break half the eggs in their confusion and chill the other half by neglect. We taxpayers will lose the entire setting bought at a high price.

I read with interest your comments on the policy of Federal relief and Federal dole. Your arguments on their face are plausible but they are not sound. This country has been a going concern for more than one hundred and fifty years. We have had droughts, crop failures, earthquakes, panics, depressions and wars, but to date none of the people have died from starvation, and through all the years we never had Federal relief or dole until recently.

This administration started out with two main

objects: "Recovery and relief." For a time it seemed that they ran along neck and neck. Now it appears that we are being "relieved" almost entirely beyond recovery.

I have always believed that in this rich country, the surface of which we have barely scratched, there is no need of a Federal dole. Charity not only begins at home but it is strictly a local matter. Relief cannot be distributed fairly or economically a thousand miles from base. The government at Washington was intended as a fortress of liberty and not a storehouse for the needy. If we are going to convert Uncle Sam into a daily Santa Claus we should tear down our Statue of Liberty and build in its place a silo or a grain elevator.

Last week Charlie told me about an incident that made my blood boil. He said that the district relief coordinator called upon him and asked him how many people were on relief in this county. He told them that he had only thirty-seven persons whose only source of livelihood was Federal dole. Then the district man said to him: "You must put some more people on relief, otherwise you'll lose your job. They'll place them in charge of the relief agent for the adjoining county."

Think of it! The Federal government, through its blustery bureaucracy, is begging self-respecting and independent citizens to become dependents. How long can this nation stand such punishment?

One of the worst things about Federal dole is that it costs millions of dollars to maintain an army to dispense it. It swells the army of bureaucrats. These white collared fellows are spraying public funds, like rain water, throughout the country. If the administration had pro-rated so much Federal dole for each county and sent the amount agreed on to the county court there would have been more relief and less waste. By the time a dollar is sent from Washington through a long line of salaried white collared men to a feeble old woman in Brookfield, Missouri, there is practically nothing left of it except the inscription "In God We Trust."

Last summer some of the farmers went to town to employ men to help in the harvest. In many cases they were unable to induce even the unemployed men to accept work. The answer was that they were on the dole and if they accepted work it would be withdrawn. I understand these instances could be multiplied a thousand times all over the country. It is unfortunately true that there are a great many people who would rather exist on a few dollars a month received as dole than to really live on wages obtained from the sweat of their brow.

I wish that we had in the White House a Chief
Executive of the type of Grover Cleveland. Grover Cleveland filled the presidential chair completely. He did not rattle in it. He possessed intelligence, courage and patriotism. He was not
only the author of the statement that "a public
office is a public trust" but on another occasion,
when drouth sufferers in Texas, some forty years
ago, petitioned the Federal government for aid
in the sum of $30,000 he said:

> "Though the people support the govern-
> ment the government should not support
> the people."

With love and affection, I am

Your Dad,

Van Clere Ball

XIV

FARMING IS A VOCATION

Huntingdale, Missouri,
February 22, 1934.

Mr. James Ball,
Colvard College,
West Plains, Virginia.

My Dear Son:

This is Washington's birthday and a holiday. More than ever, it is fitting that we set aside a whole day for recalling the heroism and honoring the memory of George Washington. If he should return to the United States in the flesh, I wonder if he would recognize it? We are rapidly drifting away from his wisdom and teachings.

A short time ago, Congress, at the request of President Roosevelt, voted to recognize Russia as a sister nation. I am wondering, as Senator Carter Glass of Virginia said, whether even Russia would recognize us, now.

In your last letter you said: "There is no money in farming." I gathered you meant that there is no chance of a farmer becoming rich, according to modern standards. It may be that you have concluded that I am a failure in life because I have accumulated only a very small portion of this world's goods.

But what is success? A man who works, rears a family and supports it, affords his children the advantages of church and school; who lives peaceably among his neighbors and pays his debts with money obtained from his own efforts is a success, according to my old-fashioned ideas.

Teaching and preaching are not money-making professions, but you would not say for a moment that there were not thousands of successful preachers and teachers.

Farming is not a business, it is a vocation. It provides a means of obtaining a livelihood in a quiet, peaceful way. From the first day I began farming until now we have always had shelter, good clothing, plenty of food, fuel, and all the necessities of decent living. In later years we have had some of the conveniences and luxuries, including the delivery of mail by the government to our gate, electricity, telephone, automobile and radio. We have had inventions which have lightened the burdens and reduced the drudgeries. In addition to all of these we have had many blessings, including good health, for which the out of door life is partly responsible; good neighbors whose latchstring hangs on the outside; a nearby school, a church and a limited number of books, magazines and newspapers.

In this connection I'll confess I probably read the newspapers more than I should but I will never forget the statement of Thomas Jefferson who said:

> "I would rather live in a country with newspapers and without government, than in a country with a government but without newspapers."

The greatest blessing of all, next to freedom of worship, has been my right, for forty years, twenty-four hours a day, to conduct my farm as I saw fit, without interference from any government agent.

In return for the privilege of enjoying these things I have been called upon to pay taxes on my farm, and, until a few years ago, I did so gladly. Formerly the tax collector appeared like a pigmy to me—now he resembles a giant. But I would not exchange my farm and position today for the lot of any millionaire. It would bring burdens and responsibilities which I would not care to assume.

To me, the "more abundant life" means peace of mind, not a long list of possessions.

Affectionately, I am

Your Dad,

Van Cleve Ball

XV

IS UNCLE SAM FACING BANK-RUPTCY?

Huntingdale, Missouri,
April 10, 1934.

Mr. James Ball,
Colvard College,
West Plains, Virginia.

Dear Son:

In one of my letters I referred to Federal dole and tried to point out some of the bad features of it. One of the worst is that it is adding billions of dollars to our National debt, and the strain of the burden is breaking the spirit of the people. I have about come to the conclusion that Andrew H. Brown, formerly of Weber City, and Franklin D. Roosevelt, formerly of Hyde Park, are the only citizens who talk in terms of billions exclusively.

I heard a few days ago that a man in Western Kansas had written to Washington suggesting that the government level the Rocky Mountains for the purpose of removing a barrier which now prevents rain clouds from reaching the dry plains of Kansas. According to the story an official in Washington answered the letter and said that the

government would not be able to consider it because, after investigation, they concluded that the
cost would not be sufficient to justify its being
classified as a **major** project.

I am not a financier but the extent of our National debt, which amounts to about thirty billion
dollars, is staggering to me. I feel like we are
all living at the base of an active volcano.

The National government in round figures is
spending:

> Every month—$700,000,000.00
> Every day   —$ 23,000,000.00
> Every hour   —$ 1,000,000.00

In addition to this we have state taxes, county
taxes, school taxes, gasoline taxes, sales taxes, and
other taxes, seen and unseen. They have multiplied like English sparrows. We are being smoth-
ered with public debt and burdened well nigh unto
death with taxes.

Today the average man with property or business feels like giving up everything and going to
some foreign country, the Lord knows where, just
to avoid the tax collectors. Most of us feel like
saying, "excuse us for living."

The President has broken all records in liberal-
ity with money belonging to other people. There
is an impression that Federal funds come from

some hidden source and do not cost the people anything; that they are a kind of manna; or, something which just bubbles up in Washington from
some deep spring.   This, of course, is a dream.   Every dime in the treasury must come from individuals who live in states, cities, counties and towns.
They deposit their money in banks and the banks,
in turn, lend it to the government through the
purchase of government bonds.

I was much impressed with what Senator Glass
said recently with reference to this matter.   He
spoke as follows:

> "Let me discuss, as discreetly as I may,
> the situation in that respect.   The existing
> outstanding indebtedness of the United
> States is approximately $28,000,000,000.
> Of that amount $15,364,000,000 is piled
> up in the banking institutions of the coun
> try.   Some of the banks have as much as
> 60 per cent of their entire assets invested
> in government securities.   The banks have
> been brought to a state in which they are
> literally obliged to take Treasury issues.
> They are compelled to take them in order
> to maintain the bond market of the United
> States, because a depreciation of ten per
> cent in government bonds would render
> insolvent 90 per cent of the banks of this
> country."

There will be no sound recovery in this country
until the budget is balanced; useless boards and bu-

reaus are abolished; and we reduce the total cost of our Federal government to three billion dollars per year or less. I am beginning to feel that the budget is not the only thing in Washington that is unbalanced.

Kansas, though hard hit by the droughts and depression, is actually reducing her taxes. What we need during the next few years is a strong, sane, vetoing president—someone who will guard the Treasury and have the courage to say "No," and the statesmanship to veto.

I wish that we had a Cleveland or a Coolidge at the helm.

With love, I am

Your Dad,

VanCleve Ball

P. S. I am enclosing a letter from my old friend, Col. Waters, ex-congressman. He is well informed. I wrote him a few days ago and asked him for some figures on the National debt. I am enclosing his letter which contains valuable information:

Little Grant, Missouri,
April 4, 1934.

Mr. VanCleve Ball,
Huntingdale, Missouri.
Dear Friend Van:

I received your good letter a few days ago and

I hasten to reply. I have gathered together a few figures which I am setting out.

When Woodrow Wilson became President in 1913, our Federal government owed less than one billion dollars. Today the annual interest alone on our National debt amounts to nearly one billion dollars. In the one hundred twenty-three years from the first inauguration of George Washington to that of Woodrow Wilson the total cost of operating our National government was about twenty-four billion, five hundred million dollars. This included the cost of the war of 1812, the Mexican war, the Civil war, and the Spanish-American war, yet this administration of Franklin Roosevelt's has either expended or authorized to be expended about twenty-four billion, two hundred fifty million dollars. This sounds incredible but it is true, nevertheless.

At the end of the World War, or shortly thereafter, the total National debt was twenty-six billion dollars. During the administrations of Harding and Coolidge and the first part of the administration of Hoover this debt was reduced to less than sixteen billion dollars. In the last four years it has climbed again to about thirty billion dollars.

The President, in his message of January 1st, this year, estimated that the public debt would amount to thirty-one billion, three hundred thirty-four million by June 30, 1935. This would represent an increase of almost ten billion, five hundred million dollars since his inauguration. It would be approximately five billion more than the amount of our public debt immediately following the World War. At this rate our National debt by 1936 will probably reach thirty-five billion dollars.

Although President Roosevelt, during his campaign, pledged "abolishing useless commissions and offices and consolidating departments and bureaus, etc.," yet, during the first year of his administration thirty-seven new bureaus have been added and new ones are hatching every day.

I am enclosing herewith figures which show the rapid increase in the annual cost of our Federal government for ten years:

Year	Total Expenditures
1926	$3,584,987,874
1931	4,219,950,339
1934	7,243,725,625
*1936	8,620,000,000

*Estimated

Kindly remember me to Mrs. Ball and to all other members of your most extraordinary family.

Your friend,

James Waters.

XVI

NATURE NOT UNDER THE AAA

Huntingdale, Missouri,
July 4, 1934

Mr. James Ball,
Colvard College,
West Plains, Virginia.

My Dear Son:

I went to town yesterday to buy a pair of overalls and also some cement to fix the cellar. I
found that the prices had doubled. Two years ago
overalls sold for about 70c; today the price is
$1.35. Cement during the same period has in-
creased in price from 35c to 70c per sack. I
came home without buying anything. They say
that farm products have increased in price, but
the trouble is that many of us farmers have no
crops this year, to sell.

According to the government report the state
of Kansas in 1932 produced 252 million bushels
of wheat. The price in Kansas City November 1
of that year was about 40c per bushel. The estimated crop for this year (1934) is 60 million
bushels and the price in Kansas City is about 75c
per bushel. The 1932 Kansas crop was worth ap-

proximately 100 million dollars at a low price, and this year's crop is worth 45 million dollars at a fair price.

I am not a supporter of this new school which advocates the policy of scarcity and high prices. I would rather raise 1,000 bushels of wheat worth only 50c per bushel than to raise only 200 bushels of wheat worth $1.00 per bushel, or, have no wheat at all, worth $1.50 per bushel.

At the close of my last letter I referred to Cleveland and Coolidge, and complimented them. Your mother read the letter before I mailed it. She took me to task for referring so favorably to President Coolidge. Her partisanship never relaxes. Political prejudice influences the lives of many people to their injury. It has completely warped the lives of some good citizens.

For president we have had in the past Federalists, Whigs, Democrats and Republicans. Some of them were very able men; others had just average ability, but all of them, without exception, were patriotic. Not one would have hesitated to sacrifice his life, if necessary, to preserve, protect, and defend the Constitution of the United States. It is true that all of them believed in what we now call "rugged individualism." This policy is not ideal and never will be. There is nothing ideal which is human, but, in my opinion, "rugged individualism" practiced by our former presidents is much better than ragged regimentation which President Roosevelt seems to favor.

I am planning to go to Texas within two weeks to wind up the estate of your Uncle Tom. Among the assets he had a small cotton farm near Corpus Christi.

Hoping that you will have time to write us fully before I leave, I am, with love and affection.

Your Dad,

Van Cleve Ball

P. S.

When in town yesterday three men on the street, one after another, begged me for money. Not one of them asked for a job.

We are having a terrific drought. There will not be enough corn raised in Missouri this year to repay the farmers for the seed planted.

It is now plain to most of us that nature is a better hand in disposing of surpluses than Mr. Wallace. Nature is not under the AAA. It pays no attention to man-made schemes, or to soothing fireside chats and the orders of bureaucrats. The law of gravity and the laws governing the temperatures and the seasons vitally affect human comfort, but they defy congress.

The law of self-preservation is another law which congress will never be able to repeal. In silence it operates without expense to the government which probably explains why it is so unpopular with the New Dealers.

If I cannot make a profit raising hogs, I will stop raising them, at least for a time. It is not necessary to pass a law compelling me to do it. It would be useless to have a bureaucrat order me to stop raising hogs at a loss. Under the law of self-preservation, I will start raising something else. I will diversify, probably raising more sheep, more cattle, and more poultry.

For some reason this administration has failed to credit the people with any intelligence, or ingenuity. The college professors in all of their planning apparently ignore Providence, the laws of nature, and the intelligence of the American people. Even the president seems to regard us farmers as so many cattle to be herded, corralled, lassoed and branded.

                                        Dad.

XVII

CONTROL WORSE THAN BOLL WEEVIL

Huntingdale, Missouri,
August 10, 1934.

Mr. James Ball,
Colvard College,
West Plains, Virginia.

Dear Son:

I returned yesterday from southern Texas. I was in a gulf storm and nearly lost my life, but I escaped any injury. The people down south are still hopeful that conditions will improve. They say that there will be a change for the better this fall. That means, of course, as Will Rogers would say, we are going to have a late fall.

We reached your Uncle Tom's farm on Saturday, July 21st. We went over the same road we did last year when we saw farmers plowing under thousands of acres of cotton just ready to be picked. I said to myself then—"that while 'Only God can make a tree,' Secretary Wallace is trying to destroy everything we see."

We went past the little harbor at Corpus Christi. For the last ten years during the cotton picking season I have seen as many as six or eight ocean

liners, in that harbor, floating the flags of Japan,
England, Holland, Germany, and other foreign
countries. On this trip I saw only one freighter
taking on cotton. The government had pegged
cotton at a price higher than foreign buyers were
compelled to pay in other countries. These foreign buyers are under no law requiring them to
cooperate with the college professors in their
scheme of planned economy, and a "recovery"
which is being delayed from month to month.

When we reached the farm I never saw a more
beautiful sight—160 acres of cotton standing
waist high and half of the bolls opened up. It
looked like a heavy blanket of snow. But there
were no cotton pickers at work. I asked Brown,
the tenant, why they were not picking cotton. He
said, "We haven't received any tags. Under the
new Bankhead Control Act it's illegal to offer
cotton for sale unless it has the government tags
on it." He went on to say that the farmers there
would take no chances in violating the law because
they did not want to be fined, or go to jail. He
said they had written, wired, and telephoned to
Washington for tags.

Then I told him to start picking cotton Monday
morning, tags or no tags; that no court in America
would fine or imprison a farmer for selling cotton
which he had raised on his own farm by the sweat
of his own brow.

On Monday he started picking and continued until Tuesday afternoon when it began to rain. For 36 hours thereafter, we had a terrific tropical storm with wind and rain. The cotton which had opened up was either driven into the soft, mushy field or carried out into the open sea.

On Thursday morning we went out to the fields. Nothing remained but the stalks. I talked to bankers. They estimated that the total loss in that county and the two adjoining counties would amount to 15 million dollars. It cost your Uncle Tom's estate about 50 bales worth $60.00 per bale. There was nothing to be done. Government inter-meddling had delayed the picking of cotton until the storm came and destroyed it.

While there I read a Houston paper containing the following interview from a man engaged in the cotton business in southern Texas:

"Our competitors have annexed our markets and our government holds half a year's crop that it does not know what to do with. * * * If we continue the present policy of attempting to make the market pay through planned scarcity, we must face the eventual loss of all our export markets for cotton; we must find some other use for 25 million acres of agricultural land, most of it in the Southwest, and some means of livelihood for one and one-half million southern families."

I stopped a day at Dallas. While there I learned that the government was lending money to a manufacturing company located there and engaged in making cotton gins to be shipped to Brazil. I mention this only to show how the government is not only cutting off foreign markets from the cotton growers of the South by pegging the price of cotton but it is indirectly aiding foreign governments to obtain machinery with which to take over our foreign trade.

Why not amend our patriotic song of "America,"—bring it down to date and have it read:

"My country 'tis of thee,
Sweet land of lunacy."

With love, I am

Your Dad,

Van Clere Ball

XVIII

"FORGIVE US OUR DEBTS"

Huntingdale, Missouri,
September 23, 1934.

Mr. James Ball,
Colvard College,
West Plains, Virginia.

Dear Son:

I am sorry to learn that my letter of August
10th reached you ten days late. You should file
a complaint with Postmaster General Farley; but
he is so busy strutting around the country brag-
ging and boasting that he will probably not see
your complaint for a year or so after you file it.
President Roosevelt certainly robbed New York
City of aldermanic material when he appointed
Mr. Farley to the cabinet. Every time I hear him
on the radio I am reminded of an experience I
had while in the legislature:

I attended a banquet. A lawyer who uses big
words was on the program. Sitting directly in
front of the toastmaster was a man who, during
the banquet, became intoxicated and buried his
face in his arms resting upon the table. After the
lawyer had **e pluribus unumed** for about five min-

utes they all engaged in a hum of conversation. The toastmaster tried to protect him. Finally, he rose to his feet, seized the gavel and said: "Gentlemen, we must have order." At the same time he came down with his gavel and accidentally struck the drunken man on the head. The latter, after four or five seconds, slowly opened his eyes and looking up at the toastmaster said: "Hit me again, I can still hear him." Like this fellow, I would rather be struck by a gavel than to listen to Mr. Farley.

The corn crop is almost a complete failure. I never saw the soil drier than it was last summer. In places there were cracks in the ground three inches wide. A drought, however, is not necessarily a calamity. It is one of nature's ways of building up the soil. Land must contain some nitrogen.

From 1915 to 1930 we had many wet, rainy seasons. The rains washed much of the nitrogen out of the soil. The moisture bred insects which were very damaging to crops. It also soured the soil. We need droughts occasionally. Nature guards the soil much better than some of us farmers do. The hot burning sun and the droughts have destroyed the insects, sweetened the soil, and put back nitrogen and other gases. For the next ten years we will probably have better crops than we have had for a long time.

Affectionately,

Your Dad,

Vau Clене Ball

P. S.

We did not return from church today until after two o'clock. The church is having financial difficulties. You probably remember that several years ago we sold the old frame church building to the colored Methodists. They paid cash for it and it is still clear. We built a new brick church and, not having enough cash to finance it, we borrowed $15,000.00 from an insurance company. The note is falling due. Pay day has arrived and the company is asking payment, and we have no money.

During the last two years every time the congregation said the Lord's Prayer it came out strong on "Oh, Lord, forgive us our debts."

We made a mistake. When we built the church we placed on it a fancy belfry and this mortgage, then dedicated it "subject to all encumbrances of record." Lightning struck the belfry and practically wrecked it, but the mortgage is still on the church.

Dad.

XIX

YOU CANNOT EAT IDLENESS

Huntingdale, Missouri,
October 15, 1934.

Mr. James Ball,
Colvard College,
West Plains, Virginia.

My Dear Son:

As I understand, your Economics professor has asked you to give in class the meaning of the processing tax and how it operates. I will try to explain it. It does not apply to all kinds of livestock and products of the soil, but only to cotton, wheat, corn, hogs, tobacco and rice.

Since Missouri is neither a wheat nor cotton country I will explain the processing tax as it affects hogs. The government imposes a tax of $2.25 per cwt.; the packer buys the hog from the farmer; when the packer sells the carcass to the butcher he adds the processing tax; the butcher then sells the carcass piece-meal to his customers, including your sister, for example, in Chicago. On the first of the month your sister pays $20.00 to the butcher. Fifteen dollars of that amount represents the price of hog meat, and $5.00, approximately, the processing tax.

Then the butcher remits the $20.00 to the packer less his profit, if any; the packer keeps $15.00, representing the original cost of the hog, plus his profit, and sends $5.00 to the United States government. The government, in turn, through the AAA, sends the $5.00 to a farmer who may not have produced any hogs at all under a contract with the government in which he gave up his right to raise hogs for a year in consideration of the government paying to him a definite amount to be derived from processing taxes.

In her last letter your sister complained about this tax. She said that for every $20.00 they spent for hog meat they obtained $15.00 worth of meat and $5.00 worth of "idleness" of some farmer who had agreed with the government not to raise hogs. I quote from her letter:

"They say you can't eat the Constitution. Well, I happen to know from experience you cannot eat idleness either, even though you have paid for it."

She also said that the price of bacon was so high that they had stopped using it and were eating more fish, and other makeshifts.

There are millions of people obtaining their living direct from the soil who do not participate in this processing tax scheme. There is no such tax on cattle, sheep, poultry, dairy products, hay, vegetables, fruit, and other products. On the other hand, the farmers and ranchmen engaged in raising such stock and products, are subject to all of the processing taxes on cotton, corn, hogs, wheat, tobacco and rice.

Again, the processing tax is just an extra burden on the small farmer who raises only one or two litters of pigs per year. He cannot qualify to take advantage of the tax. Other small farmers raising other products which I have mentioned, in small quantities, cannot qualify. They, likewise, are subjected to all of the burdens of the tax without receiving any benefits from it. Then, again, the farmers who raise only a small patch of cotton, a few acres of wheat or a few litters of pigs each year, are obtaining practically nothing net out of the processing tax even though they are able to qualify and attempt to obtain its benefits.

I have never signed a corn-hog contract with the government but one of my neighbors who signed one, sold 25 hogs last year. His gross benefit under the tax was about $125.00. Out of this he had to pay between $10.00 and $15.00 distribution expense. He told me the other day that when he finished paying for his clothing, overalls, sacks, flour and tobacco, all of which carry a processing tax, that his net return would not be sufficient to repay him for his trouble. In other words, the small producer of wheat, cotton, corn

and hogs, everything considered, is probably breaking even.

It requires fertile soil to raise wheat, cotton,
and corn. The big cotton, wheat, and corn farmers are making money out of the processing tax.
They are the ones who need it least of all. But,
the big farmers altogether constitute only a small
percentage of the total producers of livestock and
agricultural products.

According to an official government report, I
have on my table, the total number of acres of
farm lands in Kansas in the year 1934 was slight-
ly more than 48,000,000 acres,

Sown in wheat.................8,323,000 acres
Planted in corn ....3,021,000 acres
BALANCE, more than 37,000,000 acres

The 37 million acres were used in raising grass,
oats, barley, rye, mixed grain, flax, sorghum, su-
gar beets, Irish and sweet potatoes and hay, which
products were not under the processing tax. This
proves that it aids some of the farmers and burdens others. Those who are helped are in the
minority.

With love,

Your Dad.

Van Cleve Ball

XX

"WHOSOEVER HATH NOT"

Huntingdale, Missouri,
November 15, 1934.

Mr. James Ball,
Colvard College,
West Plains, Virginia.

Dear Son:

I am glad you liked my explanation of the processing tax. You ask me now what I think of it
as a governmental policy. Well, I am opposed
to it. It is destroying the farming industry and if
it is not abolished it will destroy the United States.
You may remember Thomas Jefferson once said:

> "Were we directed from Washington
> when to sow and when to reap, we should
> soon want for bread."

You cannot select any politicians who are smart
enough to run our business for us and yet that is
what they are now undertaking to do. They cloud
up frequently but they never rain. Last week, for
example, I cut the enclosed clipping from a Monroe County (Missouri) paper. It appeared in the
issue of June 8, 1934. Here it is:

> "Corn and grain sorghum may be plant-
> ed in excess of the amount permitted after

a date to be set by the Secretary of Agriculture. * * * The Secretary may set a date when such corn and grain sorghum planted for fodder must be harvested."

This shows that the farming industry is treated as a sort of kindergarten and Secretary Wallace is in complete charge of us beginners. At the rate they are going it won't be long before we will have to obtain a permit in writing before planting corn. They will probably require that no farmer can plant corn unless accompanied by two inspectors. We will have the right to work but will be denied the privileges of ownership.

Many of the farmers have not only leased their lands to the government, but they have bartered away their rights to direct their own affairs in return for a mess of pottage in the form of a processing tax. According to my views, it is a policy of making the farmer grow or not to grow what the government dictates; of destroying crops and livestock in order to create artificial scarcity; of paying producers not to produce in order to prolong the scarcity. It is a policy which is impossible to police and which, consequently, is a temptation to trickery and fraud on the government.

What are the results of the processing tax? It is changing the United States from a food exporting nation to one which now cannot feed itself. Foreign nations will soon be shipping into this country beef, butter, wheat, oats, barley, and corn. It is a policy which will enrich foreign farmers at the expense of American farmers. It will, sooner or later, strangle the American farmer to death. As a class, farmers are not faring well now. Under the processing tax their condition will grow worse. It is the old story:

> "Whosoever hath not, from him shall be taken even that which he hath."

I read in the Farm Journal a few days ago a letter written by a stockman living near Centralia, Missouri. He wrote:

> "It is figured conservatively that two million foreigners were employed to raise the wheat, corn, oats, and cattle which the AAA permitted to pour into the United States this year. This swelled our relief rolls."

This sums up the situation. It comes from a practical stockman and dirt farmer. Thoughts like these would never come from so high a source as the Secretary of Agriculture.

With love,

Your Dad,

VanCleve Ball

XXI

OUR LIBERTIES NOT FOR SALE

Huntingdale, Missouri,
January 15, 1935.

Mr. James Ball,
Colvard College,
West Plains, Virginia.

My Dear Son:

Your letter of the 10th came yesterday. You asked me what I think of the Townsend Plan. I hardly know what to say. Some people, it seems, are trying to invent an ointment to take the place of sweat. The plan is one of those things you cannot approach with thought—you have to go into a trance and dream of it, like you would dream of a rich half-uncle with a large family living in Australia, who you hope will remember you in his will.

As explained to me, it would cost the government twenty-four billion dollars annually to give every person over 60 years of age a pension of $200 per month. It would take all persons between 40 and 60 to collect the taxes to meet the payments; it would require all persons between 20 and 40 to police the pensioners and see that they spent the money and did not bootleg it to poor relatives. All minors under 20 would, undoubtedly, live with their grandparents. I have not figured out what would happen after the first month.

You speak of working several nights until ten o'clock on your debate. I caution you against working too hard. Moses said that out of every seven days we should work six and rest one. I have always sided with Moses. Providence, for some reason, made us six day clocks. If you work more than six days out of seven it is unfair to yourself. If you do not work, or at least keep busy, five or six days a week it is unfair to society.

Like you, I was amazed at the president's request for an appropriation of four billion eight hundred million dollars, without any strings. If congress complies, it will be the largest sum of money ever turned over to any person, living or dead, for any purpose. It involves more power and money than any president except President Roosevelt ever had the nerve to request. No one seems to know for what purpose this fund will be used, if voted.

We have an election in 1936, at which the president, one-third of the senators, all of the congressmen, many governors, and other officers will be elected. It may be there is some secret plan of spending this money to help the president to be re-elected. It may be a campaign slush fund. With this money they could hire millions of men to rake leaves for a year, winter and summer. By the time of the election, we will have more well-raked leaves than any other nation in the world. You will recall Edmund Burke once said:

> "I do not know the method of drawing up an indictment against a whole people."

By the same token, I say that you cannot buy the American people with five billion dollars. They will not sell their Americanism for that sum or any other sum of money. Their liberties are not for sale! The farmers, as a class, are hard-headed, patriotic citizens who can see through shams and fake schemes just as quickly as any other class of persons.

I must close this letter and go to feed the stock.

With love, I am

Your Dad,

VanCleve Ball.

VanCleve Ball

P. S. When all's said and done, what does it profit anyone to gain a few crumbs of dole and lose a whole wagon load of liberty? I never saw an animal in a zoo that wouldn't have risked its life to exchange the "security" of the iron cage for the freedom of nature. Animals are not so dumb after all.

XXII

THE SUPREME COURT OUR GIBRALTAR

Huntingdale, Missouri,
May 25, 1935.

Mr. James Ball,
Colvard College,
West Plains, Virginia.

Dear Son:

I have been so busy for the last two months I have failed to write. Furthermore, there is very little to tell you. We are still going through a long, dark tunnel of new deal experiments. Since congress voted to give the president four billion eight hundred million dollars, it is practically certain we will have a national debt of thirty-five billion dollars by July 1st, 1936. You have no conception of the meaning of thirty-five billion dollars. The same is true of myself and every other person. No mind can even begin to grasp it. The other day I received a government report from William L. Austin, Director of the Bureau of Census. The report shows that on January 1, 1935, there were:

Total farms in the U. S..............6,812,049
Total value including all
    buildings and im-
    provements thereon..$32,884,324,378.00

In other words, if all the farms in the United States were sold today for cash at the value placed upon them by the new dealers and the proceeds turned over to Mr. Morgenthau to apply on our National debt, we would still probably owe three thousand million dollars on July 1, 1936. These figures explain the reason why capital is timid, business is sick, and industry has high blood pressure. I ask whether Uncle Sam is facing bankruptcy?

I suppose you have read about the recent decisions of the Supreme Court. We still take the Kansas City and St. Louis papers. The bank takes the Chicago papers. The court, apparently, put an end to the N.R.A. The people who prepared this New Deal legislation never read the Constitution, I am sure. If the New Dealers ever studied it, it was through some kind of a correspondence course. It is not enough for an official to take an oath that he will support the Constitution—he should know in a general way what it contains.

I gathered that the Supreme Court ruled against the N. R. A. on the ground that dressing a chicken in New York City, shipped in from another state, is not regarded as a part of an interstate transaction, but strictly a local matter.

The court also held that the Frazier-Lemke law (the farm mortgage moratorium law), was unconstitutional. This was a blessing to agriculture. That law did not benefit the farmer. It killed his money market. It was a drawback to him. It kept him uncertain as to his rights for a period of six years. It is a bad policy to nurse problems which cannot be solved. Forget them and begin giving your thought to something else. I have lost thousands of gallons of spilt milk in my lifetime, but the one thing for which I am thankful is, I did not lose any time crying over it. The Frazier-Lemke law was a complicated contraption for prolonging the agony of the borrowing farmer.

The court also decided in the case of Commissioner Humphrey, a member of the Federal Trade Commission, that the president did not have the right to remove him without first preferring charges and affording him a fair trial. Humphrey held an important position. His appointment, as I understand it, had been confirmed by the Senate. No president should have the right to remove such an appointee without first preferring charges; otherwise, too much power is lodged in the hands of one man. The Supreme Court is our Gibraltar.

We should keep in mind that there is a large crowd of quack reformers who are howling for more centralized government. To be perfectly plain, our government is a dictatorship now. Let us not deceive ourselves. We are hoping that it will not last long, but, to be honest with ourselves, we must admit that we are now under a dictatorship. No one but the dictator and his pets benefit from a dictatorship. Under democracy a citizen of humble means is much happier than a rich man under a dictatorship. One enjoys security. The other is exposed to the whims of an overlord who may, at any time, rob him of all and reduce him to slavery.

Not long ago Commander Belgrano, of the American Legion, at a meeting of veterans, said:

> "Our business is to protect America and its Constitution. If the people in Europe like Hitlerism, Communism, Fascism, Socialism, or any other "ism," that is their business; but in America we are interested only in one "ism" and that is "Americanism."

Affectionately, I am

Your Dad,

Vanllene Ball

P. S.

We have had a very cold, rainy Spring. Farmers have not been able to plant any corn. I can almost see another crop failure looming up. Business is not improving. With all of the hullabaloo and spending of billions by the government, we are still scraping bottom. Your mother has not had a new dress and I have not had a new suit of clothes for almost four years. In another year we will be candidates for membership in one of the better nudist colonies.

Dad.

XXIII

"HORSE AND BUGGY" FOR A KINGDOM

Huntingdale, Missouri,
June 15, 1935.

Mr. James Ball,
Colvard College,
West Plains, Virginia.

Dear Son:

I was glad to have your comments on the Supreme Court decisions. Since you are soon to become a law student I suppose you are taking more interest in such matters. I can see from your letters an improvement in your general information and way of viewing things. You are growing, and should continue to grow, for the next thirty years. When you reach my age you will stop growing and will be lucky if you hold your own.

To be frank, the most sickening feeling I ever had was caused by President Roosevelt's criticism of the Constitution and the Supreme Court. He claims that the Constitution belongs to the "horse and buggy age," and that we have outgrown it. To put it bluntly, I parted company with President Roosevelt on that very day.

If I remember correctly some English king once said: "My kingdom for a horse." The slogan of President Roosevelt is apparently just the reverse: "My horse and buggy for a kingdom and will throw in your Constitution."

I am opposed to him for re-election. When he took his oath of office he made no reservations. I heard him distinctly over the radio. If he did not believe in the Constitution he should have never taken the oath. If he has since changed his views he should be fair enough to resign and turn the reins of government over to some man who is in sympathy with our form of government.

Conditions change but principles do not. Has there ever been any need for amending the Ten Commandments? There are probably some persons who would prefer to see them amended to suit their own habits of living. "Honor thy father and thy mother," was sound advice thirty-five hundred years ago and it is sound today.

The President's statement about the "horse and buggy age" will defeat him for re-election, even if all other mistakes are overlooked. You will recall that Moses in a fit of anger hurled and broke on a rock the two tablets containing the Ten Commandments. Later, though permitted to see the "promised land" from a high mountain, he was denied the honor of completing the delivery of the children of Israel from bondage into the "promised land."

The "promised land" of President Roosevelt is re-election, but the people will deny him the privilege. A few days after he made the "horse and buggy" statement he wrote a letter to the Chairman of a Congressional Committee in which he said:

"I hope your committee will not permit doubts as to constitutionality, however reasonable, to block the suggested legislation."

This statement was even worse than the "horse and buggy" statement because it was in a letter which the President wrote, signed and sent to Chairman Hill.

The President, at heart, is probably not undertaking to overthrow our government or undermine the Constitution, but men like Frank R. Kent who write for the newspapers have intimated that he is shallow, and does not think anything through. Every day he receives suggestions for new schemes, many of which he adopts, without thinking them through. I am constantly reminded of the firm of Amos and Andy. Andy's answer to every proposition made to him is:

"Sounds great, what is it?"

The President flits from flower to flower and

sips a little political nectar here and sips a little there. Before he has digested it, however, he passes it out to the bedraggled public in his fireside chats.

I must close and go to the cornfield. It may be dry enough to finish planting the corn.

With love, I am
> Your Dad,

Van Cleve Ball

P. S. Charlie upset me yesterday. When I came in from the cornfield at dark he told me that he hoped I would not be so outspoken against President Roosevelt because it might cost him his job, and also because the local officials might raise my taxes.

You can imagine how this statement aroused me. I said you can't weld my lips with threats; the right of free speech was my privilege as a citizen and that I would not give it up and become a dumb, driven slave merely because he held a political job. As to the taxes, I told him I would rather pay more taxes than to surrender my right of free speech. I told him that my government belonged to me and that I did not belong to it.

Then I became a little oratorical, I suppose. I do not remember everything I said but in substance it was this:

The President was handicapped in his early surroundings. He was born on Park Avenue amid the silks and satins of a wealthy home. He spent most of his life in the atmosphere of Fifth Avenue Society and on million dollar yachts. He never built up either a business or a profession. He knows nothing of payrolls, price tags or pay-days. He does not know the meaning of overhead. He probably thinks it is some kind of an Aurora Borealis.

He knows nothing of the problems of the business man, the merchant or the farmer of the Middle West. He has lived in a penthouse far removed from the strife of the street. Like a modern political Juliet he is now endeavoring to make love to the people from the balcony. His gestures and throwing of kisses at the motley crowd below is a bit of awkward acting. After spending fifty years in luxury on land and sea he has suddenly fallen violently in love with the forgotten men.

His three years of administration present an awful picture of debt repudiation, pouring of public funds down rat holes of folly, sinful destruction of animals and growing crops, tinkering with the currency, browbeating industry, fattening bureaucra-

cy, tying business to a post and picking its pockets; encouraging moral flabbiness, lashing thrift
with a cat-o'-nine-tails, patting shiftlessness on the
back, driving capital under the porch, stirring up
class hatreds, and slamming the gate in the face of
recovery and creating a state of hopelessness and
prolonging the suffering of 125 million American
people.

When I finished this speech Charlie went out
and I have not seen him since. I went to bed ex-
hausted but I slept better than I have for two
months. I relieved my system of something that
had bothered me.

Dad.

XXIV

ROME HAD A NEW DEAL ONCE

Huntingdale, Missouri,
July 4, 1935.

Mr. James Ball,
Colvard College,
West Plains, Virginia.

My Dear Son:

I have a little time off and thought I would write you a short letter. I have listened to the radio practically all day. I did not hear a single speech by a New Dealer. I have heard several patriotic addresses. What, do you suppose, is the trouble? What is the answer? Is it possible that no one invited any New Dealer to deliver a speech, or is the administration opposed to the idea of recalling the memory of Jefferson and Washington?

Do you suppose they are trying to blot out the blue and white in the American flag and leave only the red in it? Is the administration becoming a little infected with the poison of Communism and cannot recite the Declaration of Independence without stuttering and blushing?

Is the sun going down on America? Are we

packing up for a one way trip to Russia? I would like to have your views.

I become so worked up when I think of these things I lose my appetite. My hand is shaking now so that I can scarcely write.

You know Rome had a New Deal once, but only once. She tried nearly every policy which we are trying out and it ruined the great Roman Empire. Our New Deal, therefore, is just a warmed-over deal. In the Roman Empire lunacy reached its peak during the reign of a ruler by the name of Diocletian. He was the funeral director who tacked the crepe on the door. I have been re-reading the history of his time.

First he scrambled their standards of monetary value. He tinkered with the currency. Money became so unreliable that they quit using it almost entirely. They bartered. They traded grapes for fish, goats for fuel, and, of course, that was a slow way of doing business. Confidence even in the solvency of the government vanished. Credit, both public and private, took wings and flew over the fence.

Second: He launched a public works program. He built great aquaducts, highways, bridges, public baths, stadiums and parks. The cost was raised by taxation. The burden, as usual, fell on the backs of property owners, wage earners, and men of the soil, known as **agricolae.** (That is the only Latin word I remember.)

Third: He gathered all authority unto himself. He sidetracked the Senate. He became a one-man government. Though surrounded by an army of job-holders, all schemes and plans officially came from him. He was an autocrat with a crown on his head and a volcano at his feet.

Fourth: In order to quiet the grumblings of the people and aid in "business recovery" he fed thousands of them at public expense. He ordered that all commodities be pegged at a maximum price. This placed all commerce and industry in a straight jacket. Thereafter there were no swings in prices in response to the law of supply and demand or to the effect of wars and seasons.

Fifth: To provide man power to carry on his wars he imported foreign slaves. They were not in sympathy with the Roman form of government, and when Rome began to wobble they proved to be a liability instead of an asset.

To insure the ruination of the Roman Empire he "piled bureau on bureau, commission on commission" and he appointed thousands of investigators, tax collectors, and coordinators who pried into every business. It was the greatest bureaucracy which the world has ever known, prior to the one we now have in America. They were, in fact, the pall bearers who carried the corpse to its final resting place.

If you will take the time to read Gibbon's History of the Decline and Fall of the Roman Empire you will feel that you are reading a description of the present New Deal.

Rome had one advantage over us. She had no Communists. Unlike America today she had no scheming enemies within her gates, actually plotting day and night to overthrow the government.

Affectionately, I am

Your Dad,

Vaulleve Ball

P. S. I had quite an argument today with Frank Pate. He came over to borrow my corn planter. Frank is one of the best customers the implement companies ever had. When he buys farm implements he leaves them out winter and summer until they rust away. He then borrows from the neighbors for a year or two, after which he buys new implements. I bought my corn planter the year you were born.

Frank started the argument by saying that

Roosevelt was for the poor man. I replied that nearly every one of his policies had hurt the poor man; that under the N.R.A. the small business man suffered; under the A.A.A. the small farmer suffers and, when the government builds a power line in competition with private lines the small investor suffers. I know two widows in town who own stock in a big telephone company. If the government puts that company out of business it will not only ruin these women and destroy property which is now paying taxes to the government, but it will add another long list of bureaucrats to the payroll.

Dad.

XXV

"SOAK THE RICH"

Huntingdale, Missouri,
August 20, 1935.

Mr. James Ball,
Colvard College,
West Plains, Virginia.

My Dear Son:

Congress has adjourned. This should be a great relief to everybody. A session of Congress now-a-days is almost a plague. I have come to believe that a session of Congress causes more damage to the country than a drought.

One of their last measures was the Revenue Act which should have been called "soak the rich and spite Henry Ford Act." According to the newspapers it will bring in 270 million dollars annually to the government. This will pay our deficit for about twenty of the three hundred sixty-five days in the year. It is a good deal like attacking a herd of elephants with a B.B. air rifle. This bill was a political gesture.

You cannot soak the rich by this method. You can make them pay their part but no more. They are able to protect themselves. The small man can not. The rich man, if driven to it, may move to other countries and to a certain extent he can pass the tax on to the consumer, which is nearly always done. The rich man can invest in tax-exempt securities. This has been one of the evils of this country during the last twenty-five years. Most rich men have besieged the market for tax-exempt securities. This made it easy for the Federal government and every State, County and School District to borrow money. As a result they borrowed more than they needed.

Every person should pay a fair tax on what he owns, whether it is in school bonds or a stock farm, and also upon his income, whether he is a banker, engineer or salaried man. President Roosevelt, in his speech in Pittsburgh, during the 1932 campaign said:

"Taxes are paid in the sweat of **every man** who labors. * * *"

Some say that this law is directed primarily at Henry Ford because he fought the government on the N.R.A. and won. We should remember that Henry Ford was dealing fairly with his employees long before President Roosevelt was ever known. This might be said of hundreds of other large manufacturing companies.

Some have called this bill a "share the wealth"

bill. We have had a "share the wealth" program in the United States for years. Every city and town has an annual charity drive producing money, given by those who have it, to those who need it. This is a real American "share the wealth" program. It does not increase our taxes; it does not build a bureaucracy.

It is not necessary to cripple the strong in order to aid the weak. I know from experience that a good farmer can save the thirteenth pig without starving the other twelve of the litter.

"Soak the rich" is an unsound policy. We are more or less dependent on one another, the farmer, the manufacturer, the wage earner. We are a row of dominoes and whenever you tilt a domino at either end the whole row collapses.

With love, I am

Your Dad,

VanCleve Ball

XXVI

FARM RELIEF WITHOUT TRIMMINGS

Huntingdale, Missouri,
September 30, 1935.

Mr. James Ball,
Colvard College,
West Plains, Virginia.

Dear Son:

You have requested that I write you my ideas for solving the farm problem. The farm, of course, has its problems like every other business. Farm problems will never be solved by Congress. The farmer's condition will never be improved by any kind of political magic and claptrap. Certainly his problems will never be removed by changing our present form of government to a dictatorship.

The simple fact is that in the United States we have enough land to feed and clothe 500 million people with only a population of 125 million. Our ability to produce is greater than our capacity to consume the products of the farm.

The first thing we farmers should do is to recognize this fact and reconcile ourselves to it.

This may be fortunate, looking at it through a long range telescope. If the farmers produced each year to the full extent of their capacity it would be a calamity. Within one hundred years the soil would be so run down that future generations would suffer more from a shortage of food than the farmers are now suffering from a surplus of products.

My plan for helping the farmer is very simple. Taxes must be reduced! Every farmer is compelled to pay a tax on his real estate and personal property to the State, County and School District. The largest tax is the school tax. In the middle west, owners of city real estate and farm lands have borne almost the entire burden of maintaining the public schools. This is unfair. The farmer should be relieved of a part of this burden. The sales tax is probably the solution. It is gaining a foothold here and there throughout the country. It should not be imposed in addition to other taxes, but in lieu of a portion of other taxes which we are now paying.

Then again, the farmer is in need of long term loan credit at reasonable rates of interest. Agencies should be set up which would enable the worthy farmer to borrow money from crop to crop, or for one year at a time to take care of his ordinary demands.

The government should keep open the channels of trade with foreign countries. We must have a steady outlet for our products. This may be done through trade treaties. We should keep on friendly terms with as many foreign nations as possible. We should write them on their birthdays and send them Christmas cards. Their buying, however, depends largely upon their local financial conditions. We could sell ship loads of goods to foreign countries today if we would lend to them the money to pay for them. Uncle Sam did that once. To date they have neither returned the goods nor paid the notes.

The farmer should also stop living out of tin cans, bought from the grocer. The average farmer should pay his grocery bill with his own poultry and dairy products. If he would keep a comfortable distance ahead of the sheriff he must learn to diversify. Every farmer who has 120 acres of land or more should raise a few sheep, hogs, cattle and some corn, hay, oats, wheat, poultry, fruits and vegetables. This applies to the country from Ohio to Kansas, Minnesota to Missouri. When a farmer risks everything on a corn, wheat or cotton crop and has no other grain, produce, poultry or live stock coming on to absorb the shock, in the event of a crop failure, it is too much of a gamble for him to take.

The government should stop producing more

farm lands by building dams and irrigation ditches. I understand right now the New Dealers are considering several such projects which would cost the taxpayers over 700 million dollars. It would also reduce the value of every acre of farm land we now have and lead to frequent surpluses of crops. The people may need these lands in five hundred years but they don't need them now.

Lastly, the farmers should have central organizations to gather facts and data which would be valuable to the farmers. Such organizations might assist in obtaining better freight rates, in advising the members of business and crop conditions throughout the world, and aiding in marketing their products.

With love and affection, I am

Your Dad,

Van Cleve Ball

P. S. I am enclosing herewith a clipping which I today cut from the Chicago Daily News, published by Colonel Frank Knox:

"What has the A.A.A. accomplished? * * * It has helped to transform the United States from a bountiful food exporting nation to a nation which now cannot even feed itself.

"In the first 6 months of 1935 we bought from foreign farmers 230,000 head of cattle; 3,000,000 pounds of pork; 44,000,000 pounds of beef; and 21,500,000 pounds of butter.

"We imported from foreign farms 12 million bushels of wheat; 10 million of oats; 7 million 500 thousand of rye; 4 million of barley; 17 million 500 thousand of corn.

"Grain elevators along Lake Michigan's western shore are full of foreign grain. The bins of the great mills at Cedar Rapids, Iowa, are full of foreign grain. The great government elevator at Albany, New York, the largest in the country, is chock-full of foreign grain."

The situation described in the clipping is not only a disgrace, it is disaster. Sending money to foreign farmers for crops which we can raise at home is agricultural suicide in the first degree. Nature alone would have solved our problem of surpluses. President Roosevelt and Secretary Wallace undertook to perform the functions of Providence and we farmers are now called upon to pay for their folly.

For us to import beef from Argentine and wheat from Canada is just like a cobbler sending his own boots to a shoe store to be repaired.

Dad.

XXVII

1936 PRESIDENTIAL POSSIBILITIES

Huntingdale, Missouri,
October 15, 1935.

Mr. James Ball,
Colvard College,
West Plains, Virginia.

Dear Son:

You asked my opinion as to who would be the presidential nominees next year. In reply will say that if the Democratic Convention nominates Mr. Roosevelt (which it will do) I will vote for the Republican candidate, assuming, of course, that the Republicans nominate a man of common sense and who keeps his feet on the ground.

I haven't lost my partisanship. I am still loyal to Jeffersonian democracy but I cannot, as a Democrat, vote for the re-election of Roosevelt and keep on good terms with myself. Governor Eugene Talmadge of Georgia said that Roosevelt was not a Democrat and that no one could vote for him and be a good Democrat.

Governor Talmadge comes from a rock-ribbed Southern Democratic state. He is also Democratic National Committeeman from that state.

Personally, I would prefer to vote for one of several good Democrats—men of the type of John W. Davis, Alfred E. Smith, Newton D. Baker, Governor Ely, Governor Ritchie, Owen D. Young, James A. Reed, and others. But there is not the slightest chance of the convention nominating any of them.

I would not be surprised to see the Socialists place Mr. Roosevelt's name on their ticket. They will be ingrates if they don't do it, because he has carried out their last platform almost 100%. If the Communists hold a national convention they should at least invite the President to address it.

The papers mention the names of Senator Vandenberg of Michigan, Colonel Knox of Chicago, Senator Dickinson of Iowa, and Governor Landon of Kansas in connection with the Republican nomination. I would gladly support any one of them.

I hope the Republicans will not undertake to nominate a political soloist or some kind of a superman. I like a nice solo occasionally but in a democracy there is always need for choir singing and team work. As to these super-men they never pan out.

The Republicans should also beware of a platform with trap doors and secret fire escapes. They should not attempt to substitute for a platform a Christmas tree (in their show window) loaded down with prize packages for the laborer, the farmer, the soldier and all the rest. If they try to ape Mr. Roosevelt and the New Dealers by making a lot of high-sounding but empty promises which the average man would know were impossible to perform, they will lose. They cannot compete with President Roosevelt and his advisers, in promises anyway. President Roosevelt was the most "promising" candidate we ever had.

With love, I am

Your Dad,

Van Cleve Ball

West Plains, Virginia,
October 20, 1935.

Mr. VanCleve Ball,
Huntingdale, Missouri.

My Dear Dad:

The other night I made a speech in our debating society. The question was, "Who were the four greatest presidents we ever had?" In my peroration, which I had written out, I apparently made an appeal to some of those present. I am enclosing a part of it. Here it is:

"We want a President who will be as faithful to the fundamentals of our government as the stars in their course; old-fashioned, if you please, in his support of business and political morality; who believes that a public office is a public trust; that gold in the treasury of the United States is a trust fund for the payment of legitimate expenses; who knows that public funds should never be scattered in a spray of doles, donations and decoys for votes; and who believes in and will observe the boundary line between the functions of government and private enterprise.

"We want a man who, in a period of economic stress will retain his poise; who, in a time of vulgar extravagances will practice economy and keep his simple tastes; and who, in a period of bitter campaigns, will remain serene and dignified. Above all, we need a man who in a period of false and fantastic schemes will not be swept from his moorings and drag us into alien and treacherous waters."

I received a good hand when I finished. This is my senior year. I am trying to mop up.

I enjoy all of your letters. They have been a big help to me. If I can find someone driving to Missouri at Christmas time I am going to make the trip.

With love to you and mother,

Your Son,

James Ball.

XXVIII

PREACHERS ADVISE THE PRESIDENT

Huntingdale, Missouri,
November 6, 1935.

Mr. James Ball,
Colvard College,
West Plains, Virginia.

Dear Son:

I received your letter of the 20th. I was puffed up when I read it. I would almost call you a carver in wood. You expressed yourself much better than I will ever be able to express myself. I am still a hewer of wood. It would probably be more accurate to call me just a wood chopper.

You described the kind of a man we need for President. I will undertake to fix his geography. We have had thirty-two chief executives of the United States. Virginia has contributed eight of them; Ohio, seven; the states of Iowa, Kentucky, Tennessee, North Carolina, Pennsylvania, New Jersey, New York, Massachusetts and Vermont have furnished all the rest.

The center of gravity, politically speaking, in the United States today, is in the middle west. I trust next year that the Republican party will nominate for president a man who has lived in the middle west and is familiar with the problems of the farmer.

Events are happening thick and fast now-a-days. Uncle Sam has sent a delegation of congressmen to witness the birth of the new Philippine Republic. It seems a little odd to me. The Filipinos are obtaining their full freedom just as we are beginning to lose ours.

Did you read about the poll of the farmers on the processing tax? Fewer than one million voted, both for and against the tax. This recent processing tax poll calls to mind my experience with your Uncle Tom's estate. He left a will giving the bulk of his estate to his two step-children, although he had six children of his own. His second wife thimble-rigged this deal. Of course his own children did not like it. I wrote to the step-children and asked them whether they would insist upon the terms of the will being carried out.

They replied promptly that they wanted the will carried out, that they were entitled to it. They voted in favor of receiving the cash bequests. If I had left the matter to a vote of all the children, payment of the bequests to the step-children would have been defeated. I believe this fairly illustrates the meaning of the poll of the farmers on the processing tax. Several millions of them were not even permitted to vote.

You may have read the results of the elections held yesterday. No returns have trickled through as yet from Kentucky. The report is that a number of men were killed at the polls in that state. I understand they have a law which requires the election officials to take the ballot boxes to the court houses immediately after the polls close. They do not finish the count until several days after the election. This arrangement gives them a chance to bury their dead. I do not refer to this in a joking spirit. It is a sad indictment of voting conditions in many parts of the United States.

Some people, however, do not attach any great importance to election thievery. It shows how lax and loose the moral fiber sometimes grows. Casting an illegal ballot is the lowest form of treason. It is not merely an offense against particular candidates on the ticket but it is stabbing Uncle Sam in the back. It is an insult to the American flag and to the memory of our forefathers who tried to set up a government of officials who would be selected by a majority of the real voters.

Whenever you interfere with that rule you are inviting trouble. The only purpose of a fraudulent vote, at any time, is to defeat the will of the ma-

jority. If I should ever be elected governor of
Missouri I would give the people honest elections
even if I had to call out the militia and station it
at every polling place in the state.

Affectionately,

Your Dad,

Vaullene Ball

P. S. Did you read where the White House
had mailed a letter to the clergy of the United
States asking their advice concerning proper policies? It has developed that the president's secretary copied almost word for word the appeal contained in the circular letter which Governor
LaFollette sent to certain voters of Wisconsin last
spring. I am enclosing an article containing some
of the answers sent in by various clerygmen:

The Reverend Howard Fulton of Chicago said:

> "Why should the Clergy waste time in
> seeking to advise a man on social security
> legislation who has ruthlessly broken his
> campaign promises, discarded his platform
> and repudiated the Constitution, which he
> swore to protect, uphold, and defend?"

The Reverend Robert I. Wilson of Kansas City
said:

> "Your administration has * * * contrib-

uted to the decay of self-reliance and self-respect * * * It has undermined confidence with its failure to keep a single campaign promise."

The Reverend Edgar C. Lucas of Augusta, Ga., wrote:

"I wonder concerning your place in history, Mr. President. Will your place be that of the first president * * * to raid the public treasury for campaign funds with which to overthrow the very form of government by which you were raised to power?"

I notice in the papers that the New Dealers entered into a trade treaty with Canada lowering the tariff on many products of the farm. I do not know the terms of the agreement. There were two parties to it and I have an idea that Uncle Sam was "party of the second part." Agriculturally speaking, Canada is an exporting nation. The treaty, in my opinion, will injure the American farmers. However, I am hoping for the best.

Dad.

XXIX

"MOST INFLUENTIAL INDIVIDUAL"

Huntingdale, Missouri,
November 18, 1935.

Mr. James Ball,
Colvard College,
West Plains, Virginia.

My Dear Son:

You are now 21 years of age. I failed to congratulate you in my last letter. You are reaching your majority at a time when the country needs you badly. You can work at the polls next year and cast your first vote in an election which will probably be the most important one we have ever had in the country. I am more concerned about the future of America today than I have ever been in my life.

Did you happen to read the Saturday Evening Post of October 26th? General Hugh Johnson, former Director of the N.R.A. and for two years connected with the Roosevelt Administration, wrote an article which appeared in the Post of that date. Among other things he wrote:

"Even during the planning of the New Deal there began to appear—faintly and little considered at first—pressures, and vetoes in advice, from a group then sometimes called "The Harvard Crowd," but later, on account of its leader, Prof. Felix Frankfurter, irreverently yclept the "Happy Hot Dogs."

"Shortly after election there began to occur one of the cleverest infiltrations in the history of our government. There was no noise about it. The Professor himself has refused every official connection. His comings and goings are almost surreptitious. Yet he is **the most influential single individual in the United States.**

"His 'boys' have been insinuated into obscure but key positions in every vital department—wardens of the marches, inconspicuous but powerful.

"They have had a guiding hand in the drafting of nearly all legislation except N.R.A., from which they were excluded, with difficulty, by a **tour de force.**

"To them the Constitution is just a foil for clever fencing—an antediluvian joke to be respected in public like a Sacred Cow and regarded in private somewhat as Gertrude Stein probably regards the poet Tennyson, or any other Victorian. * * *

"The Hot Dog Pressure Group which diverted the New Deal weakened party organization and conceived the "Horse and Buggy" comment after the Schechter case, is almost singly responsible for this whole condition."

Now you have the picture. I have feared for some time that the hare of Americanism was only about one jump ahead of the hounds of Bolshevism. My fears were well founded.

Dr. Frankfurter was born in Vienna. His background is not entirely American. I have felt that there were a number of advisers and would-be advisers in Washington, some of whom were well read and some of them just plain red.

In addition to the group who label themselves New Dealers (but many of whom are Communistic), there are some foreign countries in Asia and Europe which would be tickled to see the United States suffer a setback. We have made rapid strides in trade and commerce. As a competitor we are stepping on their toes. Such countries would like to clutter up both our front and back yard for a time, at least.

So now, for the first time the mysteries of the New Deal legislation have come to light. Thanks to General Johnson! Congress did not prepare the bills. The Cabinet had nothing to do with them. With the exception of the N.R.A. legislation, they were all cooked up by Dr. Frankfurter's "boys."

Your mother and I attended a lecture on Russia the other night. At the conclusion they distributed pamphlets containing a quotation from George A. Burrell, an American engineer who has spent several years in Russia. The following is the quotation:

> "As the years roll on and the story of Soviet farm collectivization is completely unfolded, it will rank with the great infamous chapter of 'man's inhumanity to man.'"

I gathered from what the lecturer said that Communism first attempts to take charge of everything, including the food supply of a nation. It confuses and browbeats the tillers of the soil who produce the food supply. If you will give to me complete control of the food supply of America, I will elect myself to office if I choose and make myself king if I dare. This kind of a program has already started in the United States.

Do you remember reading in the papers where the government financed the moving of several carloads of farmers to Alaska? Although in this country we have a surplus of fertile soil, a temperate climate, and markets which are close to the farmer, the New Dealers shipped these misguided people to Alaska to farm among the glaciers and icicles. I understand that the government has shipped several carloads of farming implements

to be used by these farmers. The growing season
in Alaska is so short that little grain can mature,
so the threshing machines, plows and mowers will
all rust and decay.

If Secretary Wallace and Professor Tugwell had
sent these farmers to the Waldorf Astoria Hotel
in New York as permanent guests and provided for
them three meals a day and a little spending money
it would cost the government in the end less than
this Alaskan wild goose chase. But this policy,
while insane from an agricultural standpoint, is
sound Communistic procedure. The Communists
would like to see the farmers bedraggled until we
are willing to wear the yoke of slavery without
a murmur.

On September 17, 1934, former Senator James
A. Reed delivered an address at the World's Fair
in Chicago, in which he said:

> "I warn the farmer of this country who
> may be enticed by arguments, or influenced
> by the bribe money paid—I warn the labor-
> er who may be allured by a promised higher
> wage that if we proceed further along this
> road of Bolshevism and socialism, the bur-
> den in the end, will be fixed upon him.
>
> *   *   *   *
>
> "The gentleman who wrecked and bank-
> rupted a printing business which he inherit-
> ed can hardly be said to have more brains
> than all the farmers of the United States.

Albeit, he has recently evinced a peculiar business sagacity. He demands that the farmers shall reduce their corn acreage by 20% and then through a corporation sells them "Wallace Hybrid Seed Corn" for $7.50 a bushel, represented to increase production 20% per acre."

These excerpts from the address of Senator Reed proves that he had seen the light more than a year ago. We farmers should not ignore the warnings of such men. They know whereof they speak. Shall we stand in battle line and fight for our freedom, or slink off to the bread line and wait for the New Dealers to dish out cold Communistic soup?

With love,

Your Dad,

Van Cleve Ball

XXX

CLOUDY DAYS

Huntingdale, Missouri,
November 20, 1935.

Mr. James Ball,
Colvard College,
West Plains, Virginia.

Dear Son:

We have had the cloudiest November on record. The sun has shone but a few days this month. In a way I cannot blame it. There is very little to shine on at this time.

I am today sending you a barrel of apples. I had even thought of sending a bushel of Irish potatoes to your landlady but I hesitated to do so on account of the new Potato Control Act, soon to go into effect. I understand the new law provides that any person selling potatoes without a government license is subject to fine and imprisonment.

According to the latest reports we now have 9,047,956 persons who receive Federal checks. They are divided as follows:

Regular employees 796,297
Legislative and judicial................... 7,005
WPA and PWA...........................2,975,000

All others, including AAA
and CCC 5,269,654

Scores of new boards and bureaus have been created since Mr. Roosevelt became President, and so far as I know none have been abolished.

There is one consolation. Mr. Roosevelt's term will expire in January, 1937, under the new amendment to the Constitution. It will be the shortest term which any elected president ever served, but it will probably seem the longest to more than a hundred million people, now living and millions of unborn citizens who will have to pay.

President Roosevelt has still not figured out a way to reduce our national debt. I noticed in the paper today that there are thirty-two men in America each with an income amounting to one million dollars or more annually. Their total incomes are less than fifty million dollars yearly. If the government confiscated their incomes entirely they would pay the present operating expenses of the government for less than three days.

If Rockefeller, Morgan and Ford each own one billion dollars worth of property and the government should confiscate their entire estates, they would pay the present expense of the New Dealers for less than five months. This means that tens of millions of us small fellows will have to dig into our pockets and help pay the debt.

Prominent Democrats everywhere are rising up and attacking the administration. I presume you have seen in the papers that Col. John H. Kirby of Houston, Texas, ex-governor Wm. H. Murray of Oklahoma and William R. Hearst, all prominent Democrats, are fighting the New Deal. Mr. Hearst in a recent article, referring to the national debt, said:

> "The result is like a ball-and-chain upon a nation's progress. The result is an almost unbearable personal burden upon every individual citizen."

Ex-governor Murray recently said:

> " 'A Tax eater' is a groveling grafter trying to get more and more of the government 'pork' money—a bureaucrat cannot and will not make an honest living by farming, by working in a factory, or by conducting a business.

> "The tax eaters live off of honest, self-supporting, self-denying, thrifty, insurance-buying citizens, by getting on the government payroll, not by election, but as an appointed bureaucrat."

The campaign is warming up. You have never written me as to whether you approve my views and will join hands with me in opposing President Roosevelt next year.

Affectionately, I am

Your Dad,

VanCleve Ball

XXXI

MY FELLOW TOWNSENDS

Huntingdale, Missouri,
December 8, 1935.

Mr. James Ball,
Colvard College,
West Plains, Virginia.

My Dear Son:

You know I have never been much of a person to believe in dreams. I have done as little dreaming, I believe, as anyone. A night or two ago I dreamed that Dr. Frankfurter, Prof. Tugwell, and Secretary Wallace had prepared a speech for President Roosevelt; that he delivered it at a meeting of Townsendites in Hyde Park. Every detail is still just as clear to me as a picture. In this speech (of my dreams) he said:

"My fellow Townsends: I am in sympathy with your plans, hopes and aspirations. In fact, I am in sympathy with everything. You know and I know that people live longer today than they did a generation ago. In America they live on and on and on. As an illustration I cite to you the members of the Supreme Court. I——"

At this point your mother rang the breakfast bell and the dream came to a sudden ending.

But what I am writing to you now is not, in any way, a dream. I am awake and in possession of my normal senses. Townsendism is the child of President Roosevelt. If he ever, in fact, addresses that group of people he will probably tell them that every man, woman and child in the United States is entitled to at least $300 per month from the government. He will probably say also that the Federal government should appoint a guardian for each child and a trustee for every grown person.

We might as well get down to brass tacks. After making all due allowances for President Roosevelt's good qualities, the bald, stark fact is that he is as unfit to run our government as I would be to run the Japanese Navy. In his Georgia speech a few days ago he accused the bankers of advising him, immediately after his inauguration, that our national credit could stand a loan of 70 billion dollars. Previously he had told the people that the country was practically bankrupt when he took the oath of office.

In the same speech he personally claimed credit for increased prices of farm products. He didn't mention the shortage which had been caused by two very bad droughts in the years of 1934 and

1935. According to his ideas shortage, scarcity, and imported food stuffs are blessings.

The President is on the defensive. Never before has he faced a real political or financial battle. Until now he has always had a downhill pull. He lost his temper when he said that his critics could be found only in "well warmed and well stocked clubs". I am one of his critics and I have never been in a "well stocked club" in my life. Furthermore, I have never even seen a yacht, Vincent Astor's or any other. The Democrats have elected three presidents in the last seventy-five years. I stood by Cleveland and Wilson to the end. I can't stand by President Roosevelt. He has used the Democratic platform as a springboard. If I stood by him I would have to be an acrobat and also a diver. Let's not fool ourselves. His defeat will put an end to all of these clap-trap cure-alls, based on free rides.

Hope you will write us soon and let us know what the sentiment is at Colvard. I am anxious to know what the people out in Virginia are thinking.

With love,

Your Dad,

VanClere Ball

XXXII

ROOSEVELT DUMBFOUNDED IT

Huntingdale, Missouri,
December 15, 1935.

Mr. James Ball,
Colvard College,
West Plains, Virginia.

Dear Son:

As you stated in your letter of the 10th, the next election is less than a year away. The solemn question is what can we, as citizens, do about it and how shall we do it? The mysteries of the New Deal have been revealed, the fallacies exposed, the masks removed. We should face the facts. The President has strayed away. He has left us. Jefferson founded the Democratic party; Roosevelt has dumbfounded it.

Under the "New Deal" we have had the winds of reform but, to date, we have not been blessed by the rains of recovery. We have had political lightning. It has struck the agricultural industry and singed it badly. Lightning struck the business man also, and while it did not electrocute him he is, for the time being, paralyzed.

A bolt of lightning struck and opened the bank vaults. The bankers, during the excitement, lost their heads and turned more than 15 billion dollars of the peoples' money, over to Mr. Morgenthau. The banks should stop buying government bonds. They should put their deposits, turned over to them by the people, into legitimate business and stop pouring them into the rat-holes of New Deal folly.

During all of this wind blowing, thundering and lightning, we can see clearly three results. The business men have crawled under the porch. They are crouched down looking out and waiting for the storm to pass. The army of the unemployed and those on relief have neither been discharged nor reduced in number. Through it all, the only things that have grown during the last three years have been our national debt and Communism. They tell me as you approach Washington they stand out more prominently than even Washington's monument.

The issues in the next campaign will not be the old-fashioned controversies between the two political parties as to proper policies **under** our system of government. The real issues will be—

Shall we cling to our present form of government or abolish it;

Shall we barter away Americanism for Communism;

Shall we continue to borrow and spend, or
settle down and settle up;

Shall we substitute lunacy for sanity;

Shall we convert democrats into bureaucrats;

Shall we share our wealth through charity
or lose it through taxation;

Shall we replace impartial Uncle Sam with
Old Mother Hubbard playing favorites;

Shall we remain idle and import food or
work and produce it;

Shall we starve the litter of twelve to feed
the thirteenth pig, or give them all a
break;

Shall we pamper or punish enemies within
our gates;

Shall we march under the Stars and Stripes
or under a crazy quilt?

These are the main issues before us. The Republican and Democratic parties have never had
any differences of opinion as to any of these questions. They have differed on the tariff, the League
of Nations, and state's rights, from time to time,
but they have never been apart on these issues.

Today we are confronted by a common foe.
It lurks within our gates. It plots and plans
in the dark to stab Uncle Sam to death. It has
enlisted in its support men high up in public and
private life. They know the art of concocting and
spraying poison throughout the land. They twist
facts into seeming fancies. They know how to

dress up in Grandma's bonnet and specks. The citizens to them are just so many Little Red Riding Hoods to be fooled, flimflammed and destroyed. They know how to juggle facts and make them jingle like gold. They know how to punctuate falsehoods to sound like the Sermon on the Mount. They have the sinews of war siphoned from the public till. They have an army of trained bureaucrats who know all the tricks of the game. I would say, therefore, that we have a dangerous foe.

For the salvation of the Democratic Party we Democrats should join hands with the Republicans in the battle. Stephen A. Douglas, when the first guns of the Civil War were fired on Fort Sumter, cast his lot with the Union and then sent this brief message to Lincoln:

"There can be no neutrals in this war."

In joining hands with the Republicans I doubt whether we are conferring any favor upon them. I do not know why any party would want the job of running this government after the New Dealers are expelled. At least for a time, it will be like taking over a Five Thousand Dollar farm subject to a Twenty Thousand Dollar Mortgage.

The Democratic Party could sue President Roosevelt for divorce on the ground of desertion and win. Personally, I would be willing for him to retain the custody of all the children born to the union since March 4, 1933.

America has not yet reached her destiny. Our future is in front of us and not behind us. Following the defeat of President Roosevelt we will have the greatest growth and prosperity which we or any other nation has ever had. Although Mr. Roosevelt refers to our great record as "ruins of the past," yet these "ruins" contain much valuable salvage. The New Deal is in the red. Furthermore, it contains no pay ore.

The Civil War is over. Let us present a united front and defeat every New Deal Congressman, regardless of party label, who may offer himself for re-election. The disciples of Jefferson and those of Hamilton, between whom today there are no material differences, should join hands to defeat the disciples of Lenin and Trotsky who are now so active in America. Let us banish them politically to the "Beautiful Isle of Somewhere," fumigate nearly everything in Washington, and then go on about our business.

PAY DAY is here!

Affectionately, your Dad,

Vanllere Ball

MESSAGE ON "STATE OF UNION"

Huntingdale, Missouri,
January 5, 1936

James Ball,
Colvard College,
West Plains, Virginia.

Dear Son:

You've gotten back to college by now. I see that Col. Lindbergh and his family in their flight from American kidnappers, have landed in England. This shows that good citizens can leave America in self-defense. Wait until they begin leaving to escape burdensome taxes. We'll run out of boats in a short time.

Your mother and I heard President Roosevelt's message to Congress on the "state of the Union," Friday night. That's what it was labeled. He talked about everything except the "Union." He seems to be against autocrats and dictators—in Europe. To be candid, it was political chloroform which had lost its strength.

The message showed the "state" of the President's mind made jittery by recent reports from the grass roots. The appeal to class hatreds was unpardonable. I believe that President Roosevelt would go a long way to be re-elected. The people will resort to the ballot only and defeat him over-whelmingly. They will be at the polls bright and early. They are fed up on isms, nostrums, and cure-alls. Political quackery is facing a crisis. It is on trial. Thousands of quacks will be debunked this year and, on election day, will be sentenced to hard labor.

Another thing, the next president will, undoubt-edly, be called upon to fill several vacancies on the Supreme Court. I feel that a majority of the people believe it would be a calamity if President Roose-velt has anything to do with it. If he should name a majority of the court the time-honored refrain: "The Land of the Free and the Home of the Brave" would fade out like the tinkling of a weary and distant flock; Washington would become the Western Headquarters of the Moscow govern-ment; our overgrown bureaucracy would suddenly blossom into a high-heeled and smirking tyranny; and America overnight would become a helpless, hopeless, Godless state of confusion, chaos and in-justice.

With love and affection,

Your Dad.

Van Clene Ball